Clearer Horizons

Clearer Horizons

James Allan

www.afeonline.com

Clearer Horizons

James Allan

First published in 1997 under the title of Progressive Flying by Airlife Publishing Ltd
ISBN 1 85310 819 7

This edition Published 2009 by Airplan Flight Equipment Ltd

ISBN 978 1 906559 083

Published by
Airplan Flight Equipment Ltd
1a Ringway Tarding Eatate, Shadowmoss Road, Manchester M22 5LH
Tel: 0161 499 0023 Fax: 0161 499 0298
www.afeonline.com

Contents

Introduction

When you first got your Private Pilot's Licence (PPL) from the United Kingdom Civil Aviation Authority or your JAR PPL from the European Joint Aviation Authorities you probably thought that it was rather a disappointing looking document, just a small slip of paper. But that flimsy certificate did represent something of real significance. It marked the culmination of your basic flying training, though not by any means the end of your learning how to fly.

It is the one tangible reward you get for a great deal of study, a certain amount of sacrifice, considerable mental and physical effort and a far from negligible financial investment. You have spent a lot of your time studying text books, travelling to the aerodrome (sometimes only to hang around there in less than ideal training weather, waiting hopefully to fly), and from time to time actually doing some flying training, being debriefed and travelling home again. The money you have spent to get this little bit of paper could have bought you the holiday of a lifetime, a luxury cruise perhaps, or a round the world flight. Alternatively it could have been turned into a deluxe fitted kitchen, or it might have enabled you to buy a turbo-GTI car, complete with satellite navigation, CD player and quadraphonic hi-fl, to replace the tired old vehicle you are still running.

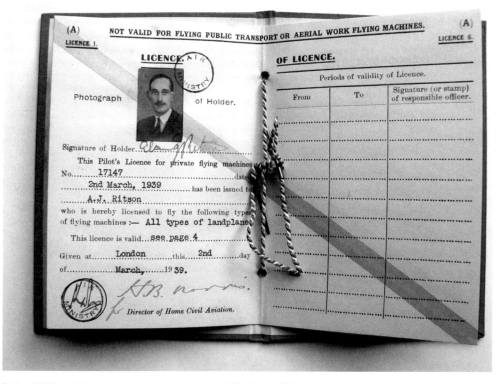

Before WW2 and for a few years after, when you qualified for a PPL you received a handsome hard-cover licence booklet from the CAA with your PPL, ratings, medical certificate etc pages secured inside it by 'boot-laces'

Later this was replaced by a little piece of buff-coloured card, but even that is slightly more impressive than the equivalent American FAA pilot certificate, which is the size of a credit card.

Instead you have acquired this little bit of buff-coloured paper? So what are you going to do with it now you have it? You can (like rather too many other people who get their PPLs) brag about your achievement and then do little more than bask in the reflected glory of being a private and qualified pilot. You can perhaps be a little more daring and make one or two Sunday afternoon trips to a neighbouring airfield and have a coffee and sandwich there before flying home again. But you will soon realise that, at real costs amounting to around £40 for a coffee and £50 for a sandwich, this isn't actually the most economical way of quenching your thirst or stilling your pangs of hunger. You will almost certainly also take some of your friends on flights that are little more than extended circuits around the airfield.

Not every GA aerodrome café is quite as attractive a place (nor perhaps serves such good food) as this one at Calais, seen here during a flying club fly-out for lunch. But more and more GA airfield restaurants both in UK and abroad are becoming well worth visiting either for the so-called '£100 cup of coffee' or for something more substantial.

Eventually you are bound to start wondering why on earth you were so stupid as to spend all that time and money on learning to fly. It is a dreadful shame how many newly qualified private pilots do have periods when they think that like this. It is all the more mortifying because your PPL can open up some marvellously enjoyable opportunities for you. It can unlock a whole new world of holidays, business and career openings. If you are one of the many pilots who are looking for some ideas about how to use their PPLs, read on a little and I think you will soon discover enough about some of these opportunities to help you to adopt a much more positive attitude towards your future as a pilot.

Danger to Avoid

The greatest danger that lies in wait for most private pilots is not engine failure, fire in the air, flight into bad weather or any of the other emergencies your instructor has just finished teaching you to cope with. Quite simply, it is boredom. Since it would be bad for business to tell you about it, I bet neither your instructor nor the management of your flying club or school were ever kind enough to warn you about this boredom. It is probably the best-kept secret of the flying training world. But it is true. After the first flush of excitement and enthusiasm it is all too easy to find the local scenery from the air getting boring; flying solo (because you have run out of friends to take flying) gets boring too; the snacks in the 'greasy spoons' of the few easily-accessible local airfields soon begin to taste even more boring; the sluggish Cessna with its draggy legs sticking out in the slipstream becomes a boring machine to fly; flying itself can be a pretty damn boring business because (thankfully) emergencies never seem to occur and you don't now have an instructor sitting there beside you ready to spring any surprises on you. Flying seems to have lost its challenge, and with it, most of its fun. But things really don't have to get like that. Honestly!

A sluggish Cessna with its draggy legs sticking out in the slipstream

Making it all Worthwhile

Instead of getting into such a frame of mind you can go ahead and decide turn your PPL into one of the most rewarding investments you have ever made. That is what this book is all about. It is for the pilot whose logbook is beginning to show longer and longer gaps between the flights it records, or where the 'From' and 'To' columns are gradually being filled up with ditto marks. It is for the owner who finds that dandelions and long grass have grown tall enough to hide the main wheels each time he or she returns to the aircraft. It is for the pilot whose left shoe soles wear out before the right ones and whose rudder leans permanently to the left from constantly flying boring left-hand circuits and bumps. It is for the pilot who is beginning to feel a bit like a tennis ball, always flying to and fro along the same unadventurous route between the same two familiar airfields.

One way of making worthwhile use of your PPL is to use it as your first step towards a Commercial Pilot's Licence (CPL) and then possibly an Airline Transport Pilot's Licence (ATPL). That way you can turn the dividend that is paid on your PPL investment into nothing less than your future career earnings. But that is not actually what *Clearer Horizons* is about. This book has been written for people who earn their living outside commercial piloting but who have been keen enough about flying for that interest to carry them through to the successful completion of a PPL course. It is written mainly for the private pilot, young in either years or flying hours, but it will also be of interest to any pilot who, regardless of age or experience, has begun to wonder 'Where does my flying go from here? What can I do with my PPL now?'

Sometimes a spell of bad weather is enough to bring this feeling on; occasionally it is a personal cash crisis. It hits other pilots shortly after they've completed an advanced rating (multi-engine or instrument flying perhaps) and they wonder then what to do next. But almost all private pilots are liable to find these feelings of doubt creeping into their minds quite soon after they get their new PPLs. They no longer have an instructor to shepherd them along; to encourage them to go that one stage further; to plan for them what they are going to do with each new hour in the air. For the first time in their flying lives they have to set their own objectives, decide their own destiny.

If you are one of these pilots, and if you are also a prudent pilot, you will soon begin to realise that completion of your PPL course hasn't magically turned you into a pilot for all seasons and all ventures. You may very well feel you have finished learning to fly. But one thing all pilots must appreciate is that a PPL is really not much more than a licence that allows you to start learning about flying. And I don't know one single good pilot who has ever reached the end of that stage of his or her education.

The aim of this book is to help you really enjoy using the privileges of your PPL by constantly extending your knowledge of flying. It is not in any way an attempt to encourage you to take stupid risks; quite the contrary in fact. But it does try to help you put into a sensible perspective some of the more alarming aspects of flying that often seem to take an altogether too prominent place in training syllabuses. You have been brought up on a diet of engine failure procedures and forced landings. The awesome power of a thunderstorm has been dinned into you over and over again. The thought of seeing ice build up on the wings of your aircraft almost certainly causes shivers to run up and down your spine. Learning how best to handle (or even better, how to avoid) situations like these has a very proper place in all safety conscious flying training, but these skeletons must never be permitted to cast their long shadows across the whole of the rest of your flying life. You have got to remain ever alert to the dangers associated with these aspects of flying and you must keep yourself prepared and in good practice to cope safely with them. However, as you will discover in later chapters of this book, there is a great deal more to enjoying the privileges of being a pilot than sitting on the edge of your left hand seat, nervously waiting for the next emergency to strike.

You will also learn here something about how to cope with weather you never met whilst training and how best to avoid the types of weather you are really better never to tangle with. You will find out the advantages and drawbacks of various types of aircraft, what they can do for you and what you can do with them. You will be shown how best you can develop new skills such as night flying; instrument flying; aerobatics; precision flying. If your basic training was done at a big commercial airport, you will be pointed towards learning how to fly safely in and out of little grass strips. If you did most of your flying training at one of these smaller, quieter aerodromes, isn't it high time you learned how to mingle competently and confidently with the airliner traffic at major airports? You will get to know and recognise your own limitations and develop the judgement and airmanship that will ensure you fly safely within these limitations.

Follow some of the suggestions here and perhaps one of these days you will find yourself having the wonderful experience of introducing your own grandchildren to the joys of flying in little aeroplanes. In this way too, you should also be able to become and stay a safe enough pilot to go on year after year enjoying all the many other pleasures and the thrills, as well as the enormous satisfaction that a private pilot's licence can bring into your life.

It really is a great experience for all involved when you introduce your grandchildren to the joys of flying in little aeroplanes

I've certainly enjoyed my flying, even right at the beginning of my piloting career when I was an engineering student and I joined the University Air Squadron as a student pilot, friends kept asking me, "Why do you like to fly so much? What is it about piloting that makes you want to go up and fly these cold draughty old biplanes around the Scottish skies?" My parents just couldn't understand my enthusiasm, nor could most of my fellow students. At that time I wasn't quite sure how to answer that question appropriately. But I think I know now.

Taking a young person for his or her very first flight is a unique experience. I remember meeting one little eleven year old girl at a Young Eagles event (see Chapter 2) who was too frightened at first even come anywhere near the plane. Then after a bit of parental persuasion she finally plucked up courage and clambered aboard. I doubt if she took in much of the pre-flight briefing but finally there she was, harness on and ready to fly. She sat silently, white knuckled (and I think with her eyes tight closed) as we accelerated along the runway and climbed gently away. "Have a look out the window now." I suggested. Eyes opened hesitantly to take the new scene in, and I sensed the tension beginning to evaporate. I banked the plane gently and pointed out her village below. That completely broke the tension and her apprehension was replaced by amazement at all the tiny houses, the miniature trees and fields. In no time she was excitedly pointing out her house, school, church and supermarket. "Look," she cried, "that's where Christine lives," blissfully forgetting I didn't even know her 'best friend'. Then, I suggested she might like to have a go at flying it herself. Terror struck again. "Oh, no, I can't do that! We'd crash for sure!" "Of course you can." I took my hands off the yoke. "Look, I'm not touching the controls and the plane is flying itself. All you need to do is gently show it which way to go." Tentatively at first, she took hold of the yoke. I explained how a push eases the nose lower and a gentle pull starts a climb. After a little squeal at the unexpected changes in the g-forces she was soon happily turning and twisting over the landscape below, and becoming very reluctant now to return to the airfield. My passenger was thoroughly enjoying herself, and her own delight reflected itself in mine. A bonus came after we landed when the she slipped out of the seat, a very different and more confident little schoolgirl than the anxious child who had climbed into it less than half an hour ago. "You know mister," she said before dashing across the apron to tell her parents all about the flight, "I'll never need to be scared of flying again." Even if, in their excitement at the adventure of flying, some youngsters totally forget to say thanks, taking them flying is still a wonderfully rewarding experience for any pilot. And that is one of the reasons I enjoy my flying.

I am cruising steadily in bright sunshine above a solid cloud base and the aircraft is approaching the destination. Now I must stop simply enjoying the view of azure blue sky above and endless billows of snow white clouds below. It's time to settle down to concentrate on the job in hand. Descending into the mounds of white cotton I lose all outside references and switch instinctively to the discipline that I learned in my flying training and have polished by experience since then. Now it is time for serious flying, for working the navigation aids and gently manoeuvring the aircraft to line up for the approach. Following the instruments and avionics I pilot the machine as accurately as I can until suddenly it breaks out of the low clouds and there is the runway straight ahead, approach and runway lead in lighting glowing white and red through the drizzly gloom. I ease the throttles closed and land with the usual feeling of immense satisfaction that comes from a safely completed instrument approach and landing. It was worth all the trials and tribulations involved in acquiring these skills and qualifying to fly on instruments. I know it isn't magic; it is nothing more than training and applied technology, but it still is something that only a very small percentage of our fellow men and women can do, it still feels like magic to me and it's all the more satisfying for that. And that is another reason I enjoy my flying.

Flying fills the mind with memories. Some scary, but most of them rather wonderful … probably because the human mind has the fortunate habit of blanking out the sorts of thing it doesn't like remembering. Some of my favourite memories include my first flight across the Alps late one evening in a tiny two seater that felt even tinier against that majestic background of imperious looking snow-covered peaks and glaciers. I felt a total intruder who had absolutely no right to be breaking the immense eternal silence of these pink-tinged mountains, not even with the gentle sound of a little 105hp engine at 10,000 feet. Then there was a New Zealand holiday when I rented a humble Cessna 150 from a club near the Bay of Islands and it became my magic carpet. It carried my wife and me to viewing Ninety Mile Beach from our aerial vantage point, to seeing dolphins playing in Whangaroa Harbour, and to circling around the lighthouse at Cape Reinga, North Island's northernmost extremity. That is where the Tasman Sea and Pacific Ocean meet in a deep blue swirl of opposing currents and where Maori folklore claims that the spirits of their dead depart New Zealand, heading north towards their own Polynesian paradise. I hope the Maori spirits didn't mind us sharing their airspace for those memorable few moments. Being a pilot has made visiting the mystical Scottish islands of Mull and Skye, the Orkneys and Shetlands, Lewis and Tiree so much easier than having to face the hassle of driving over miles of minor roads and waiting for ferries. Looking from a Skyhawk into the still smouldering volcanic crater of Mount St Helens shortly after its eruption is something you don't forget in a hurry. That is yet another marvellous memory bestowed simply because I fly. These are a few more of the reasons I enjoy my flying.

Not Canterbury in Kent but Canterbury in New Zealand. Just one of the many airfields I've enjoyed flying from in a wide variety of overseas countries.

Coming home from a business trip late on a summer evening I am piloting myself through a cold front. Ground radar has helped by pointing me away from the most active of the thunderstorms, but I am still poised in a flimsy aluminium structure between towering clouds, looking towards a distant Cumulonimbus with its castellated shape and massive anvil illuminated by the red and orange colours of the setting sun. Occasional flashes of lightning in the clouds betray something of the power and danger inside them, but somehow just add to the sheer splendour of the scene. There is no sight quite like that. Thunderstorms viewed from ground level are not in the same league. Another reason I enjoy my flying.

High above a big city on a clear winter night, I've often enjoyed a grandstand view of a spectacular light show that earthbound beings can never see. From the vantage point of a darkened cockpit a night flying pilot is treated to an inspiring panorama that is far broader than anything an airline passenger can ever see through a little cabin window. While night flying over open countryside you usually still have a fairy-tale view of far off towns looking like sparkling jewels connected by the rivers of light that are actually the main roads and motorways. Not a lot of people are lucky enough to have access to sights like these. And that's another excellent reason for enjoying flying.

And I haven't even mentioned the more practical benefits that I have found arise simply because I am a pilot. Things like three day business trips with nights away from home being turned into easy one day flights. A little aeroplane can often eliminate the journey times to and from major airports, the check in delays and all the airline security hassle involved. Yes, I've found flying on business has saved me time and reduced the wear and tear on my psyche. And I have also often found that arriving at the local airfield in your own aeroplane gives an excellent starting point for the actual business discussions. Private pilots who fly on business really do get business done.

Then I have enjoyed popping across from the mainland after work for dinner in an island restaurant off the Scottish or Danish or Greek coast perhaps, a trip that you quite simply cannot do if you have to use cars and ferries. A little four seat Piper or Cirrus or Cessna becomes a veritable magic carpet on occasions like that. Exploring a foreign holiday destination by light aircraft instead of hired car opens up a multitude of possibilities that are totally impossible and unknown to people who aren't fortunate enough to be pilots. I have seen and experienced much more of the United States, Canada, Spain, Portugal, New Zealand, Germany, France and many other countries than I ever would have been able to do, had I not been a pilot.

Taking neighbours up for a sight seeing flight is often a great way to cement a life long friendship, as is obliging acquaintances occasionally with an aerial taxi service to somewhere they want to visit. Even the much maligned 'hundred pound hamburger' flight to a nearby airfield for no more than a cup of coffee or a snack can actually be much more than just an excuse to get back into the air for a while. It works out pretty expensive for that coffee, I admit, but don't forget the enjoyment you get from these short flights themselves, the fascinating people you meet, the interesting aeroplanes you see, the chat you enjoy.

There are so many good reasons for learning to fly and then to keep on flying once you have got your licence, and so many different and enjoyable ways for you to make full and fascinating use of that private pilot's licence.

Chapter 1
Taking Care of Your Passengers

Your First Fellow Travellers

Even before you started learning to fly you probably already had a mental list drawn up of the friends you were going to take flying as soon as you got your licence. These would probably include your girlfriend or boyfriend, fiancée or spouse, brothers and sisters, parents, children perhaps, workmates and neighbours. In one way you were probably rather hoping to impress them yet in another way you were simply wanting to share with them something of your new found pleasure in being a pilot. As soon as you have your PPL in your hand, you are legally entitled to be the captain of a passenger carrying aircraft, provided of course that particular aircraft is included in the privileges of your licence. You are also entitled to defray some of the costs of your flying (as explained in more detail in Chapter 5) by sharing expenses with your passengers. It probably won't be very long after your PPL arrives when you coax the first unsuspecting soul into the aircraft with you. Some of the ideas in this Chapter should help you to make sure both you and your passengers enjoy the experience!

Many pilots annotate their logbooks with the names of the folk who have flown with them, occasionally totting them all up and claiming they have now flown more than such and such a number of passengers. A more important total, I often feel, would be the number of people who have entrusted their lives to you in the air on more than one occasion.

Attune Yourself to Your Passenger

When you are taking someone up for a flight it is particularly important that you attune yourself to your passenger's feelings. You have your piloting job to do, but spare an odd moment away from the vigilant look out, the careful scanning of the instruments and all your other duties of airmanship, to sneak an occasional glance at your companion in the cockpit. If your passenger is grinning like a Cheshire cat, all is probably going well. The whole idea of the flight is for you both to have a good time. If there is a somewhat anxious or puzzled look on the face beside you, then you really ought to try to find out what is causing that strained expression and do your best to give the necessary reassurances or answers. If there is a chalky pallor accompanied by deep breathing, locate a sick bag and head straight for home. Nobody is going to enjoy a flight under these circumstances. Being sensitive to your passenger's feelings is so much easier now that side by side cockpit seating is the norm for most light aeroplanes. I vividly remember one of my early passengers, a girlfriend I was taking up in a Tiger Moth on her very first flight. An aeroplane with tandem open cockpits, where the passenger sits up in front of you, makes it tricky to see facial expressions! Having to communicate with each other by shouting through a rubber tube with a mouthpiece didn't help much either. Just about ten minutes into the flight I saw her leather gauntleted hand jabbing vigorously towards the ground below and heard her shouting what sounded like 'I want back down' as she gesticulated. I made a gentle Rate 1 turn back towards the airfield and within a very few minutes the Tiger Moth's wheels were rumbling over the grass again. However fond I was of the girl (and I must admit I really did like her) I felt very glad we had made it back down safely before any vomit had sprayed back in the slipstream. That sort of thing can

Taking a girl friend flying in a Tiger Moth

put a strain on any friendship. Unfortunately, as soon as I shut the engine down I found myself on the receiving end of a tirade from a very disappointed and not in the least unwell young lady. 'That was one hell of a short flight! Why on earth did you turn back like that?' I explained what a considerate pilot I thought I had been; then she made it abundantly clear to me that she had not been feeling in the slightest airsick and had merely been trying to ask me 'What's that town?' Nice girl she was too; never did see much of her after that. That was my first practical lesson on how very important it can be to keep alert as to how your passengers really are feeling about the flight.

Thoughtfulness for First Timers

More than a century after man made his first powered flight; over three quarters of the British population have still never been in the air. Of those who have flown, the vast majority know flying only from the point of view of a passenger in a large commercial airliner. So, even though the environment of a little single piston engine aeroplane may have become second nature to you now, don't forget that it is most probably all totally new and very bewildering to your passengers. You owe it to them to explain things in advance. The cockpit may look quite like the inside of a car but remember to warn them that once the engine starts it is going to be a great deal noisier than inside a Toyota or a Volkswagen. Front seat passengers must be made well aware that their hands and feet should stay clear of the controls throughout the flight and they should be asked in advance not to distract you at critical times such as during take-off and landing. Instruments on the panel fascinate some passengers; tell those ones a little about what the more easily understood ones are for. Don't bore the others about the dials, knobs and switches if they show no curiosity about them. They'll get much more enjoyment from looking out of the windows. Small aeroplanes often bank more steeply than airliners do, so explain that even if the wing on their side suddenly appears to have vanished, they are in no danger of falling out. Unexpected noises can cause alarm. If the aircraft you are flying has a stall warning klaxon or bell, your passengers will appreciate knowing about it before it blasts off in their ears, perhaps sounding to them like a heavy truck trying to overtake just as you cross the threshold to land. Unexpected silences can frighten people too. Let your passengers know in advance that it is quite normal for things to go a bit peaceful as you throttle back to descend or land.

Pilots should always explain to their passengers at least something about what they see on the instrument panel

Comfort Factors

Tell your passengers, before you go out to the aircraft, that there is no toilet on board. This is probably the first aircraft they have encountered that doesn't have that important accessory fitted as standard. Show people where the sick bags are stowed, just in case someone should 'feel unwell'. (It is best to avoid using the actual word 'sick'). It is best also to avoid using lots of technical words you may well be familiar with but which are likely to be just jargon to your passenger. Trailing edge, walkway, aileron, bank, backtrack are just some of these. Most non-flyers think that 'stall' means the engine abruptly stopping, as in the case of a car engine, while the terms 'side slipping' and 'skidding' can also be alarming concepts to someone more used to driving than flying.

Unless it is a hot 'fry eggs on the concrete' day it is best to close all doors and windows before taxiing out; it makes some inexperienced passengers feel very insecure to have open gaps and draughts once you are on the move. Taxi slowly and try not to jerk passengers with sudden jabs of brake or abrupt turns. Remember that ATC radio chat is incomprehensible to most non-flyers. It is worth giving your fellow travellers some idea of what this gibberish is all about. Just imagine what the effect on a first time passenger might be on hearing what sounds like 'Deceiving your stench live; queuing ache diner hate tree; Runaway induce two sick; Queer taxi to hold a pint whisky.' And that's just before you take-off! What about a slightly anxious passenger while up in the air overhearing a reassuring transmission that seems to say something like 'Kill a Yankee's cock one for sex heaven with high dent' or some similarly baffling gobbledygook? That call might also remind you to explain why there is a green light flickering erratically on the instrument panel too. Occasionally passengers who spot the transponder light get the disquieting feeling that it must be trying to draw the pilot's attention to something that's going horribly wrong.

If your passenger has never been up in a small plane before, try to pick a nice clear day and a quiet calm air time of day for the flight. Air turbulence and gusty conditions play havoc with sensitive stomachs and peering into haze isn't going to impress many passengers with the joys of aviating in little aeroplanes. This is no time either for you to try to show your skills as a potential aerobatic ace or combat pilot. Keep the turn's gentle, climb and descend only at reasonable angles. Try to explain your manoeuvres in advance and you will find passengers much less likely to jump and clutch at the arm rest, door handle, controls or your elbow each time the engine note changes or the aircraft banks. Above all, do your best to pull off a greaser when the flight is coming to an end. Passengers all talk to their friends about their experience and what they thought of their pilot's proficiency. It may not have seemed like a particularly bad bounce from your point of view but, having nothing to compare it with, the passenger could well have a very different opinion of your landing. Just think what you would feel about the driving skill of someone who thumped the front bumper of the car into the house wall as you came back from a trip together. It is worth it, for your own esteem if for no other reason, to get good at making smooth landings and then to keep practicing to stay that way!

Experience and Safety

You might find some of your friends are a little reluctant to fly with you too soon after you qualify for your PPL. Understandably (and as it happens, quite correctly) they feel you are somewhat lacking in experience compared with an ATPL qualified pilot, and so they may not yet be inclined to risk their necks with you at the controls. You could try explaining that statistically one of the safest periods in a pilot's career covers the first few dozen flying hours after getting a PPL. You have all the training fresh in your mind and, still being a little unsure of yourself, you are more likely now than later to ask advice about anything unusual, check the weather more carefully, pre-flight the aircraft meticulously and avoid all foreseeable risks. It is a sad fact that, if you are like many pilots, by the time you have about 200 hours logged you'll begin to feel you know it all and, believing you've got enough experience now, think you can dispense with some of these 'student pilot' attitudes. The accident charts show the sad result of this. And, assuming (like the vast majority of pilots) you make it safely through that 200 hour phase, it is worth remembering there is another significant blip in the accident charts for pilots with just about 1000 hours under their belts.

Briefing is Obligatory

You may feel that giving so much information to a passenger who is just going up with you for something as simple as an extended circuit of the airfield, really is going a bit over the top. It isn't. Under the law, the commander of any UK registered aircraft (whether it is a balloon, microlight, helicopter, light aircraft or airliner) is required to ensure that a suitable briefing is given to all passengers on board. Obviously, there is no need to explain regulations about not carrying explosives, acids and compressed gasses if no luggage is involved, and how to cope with a ditching is somewhat superfluous for a 20 minute local flight around an inland airfield. But you are legally obliged to warn all passengers of the dangers of propellers, explain how to operate the safety harness, door locks, catches and exits from the aircraft (including kicking out a window should the plane overturn after a forced landing). You must explain how best they should brace themselves before any forced landing and show them where to find the fire extinguisher and first-aid kit, if any.

It is not obligatory (but often makes passengers feel they are more like part of the crew and less like useless pieces of self loading cargo) if you explain the importance of maintaining a good look out and ask them to help by pointing out any other aircraft they see (high flying jets excepted). An extra pair of eyes to cover your blind spots never comes amiss, especially when in and around a busy circuit, and the average passenger is delighted to feel useful during the flight.

Spreading the Gospel

The last thing you want to do when flying passengers is to put them off the whole idea of flying in light aircraft. Treating the flight as being primarily for their benefit and not purely for your own will certainly help prevent that happening. Once you find that the passengers you fly are really enjoying being up with you (and not just saying they do, to make you feel better) you could think about extending the range of people you carry. You will, after all, eventually run out of friends and relations, even if some do agree to fly with you more than once.

General Aviation (GA) will flourish in the future only if a regular supply of new student pilot's show up to learn and only if GA's often ill informed opposition lobby can be successfully fended off. As a good private pilot you can play your part in both of these areas. By taking along as a passenger (perhaps on a flight you were going to make anyway) some air minded youngster you know, you may be helping to produce the next generation of student pilots. In the early 1990s the American Experimental Aircraft Association (EAA) started a scheme called the 'Young Eagles' under which private pilots volunteer to give short air experience flights to children between 8 and 17 years of age. In the UK this excellent idea is operated under the auspices of the Light Aircraft Association (LAA) and by participating in this you could be helping in both ways. Some of the children you fly may well end up becoming pilots themselves as a result of the seed you have helped to sow. Others may be future local councillors, politicians or MPs who, as a result of learning at least a little about flying from their flight with you, will be more likely to look upon light aviation from a more favourable point of view. They could one day in the future decide to approve, instead of oppose, a planning application for a new airfield, or maybe even ensure that the interests of GA are not forgotten in some future transportation white paper.

Message for the Media

You might also like to consider flying yet another category of passenger. GA and light aircraft in particular, tend to get a pretty raw deal from the media. A lot of the inaccurate news coverage that you read is not so much biased as simply uninformed. By writing and reporting like this, news reporters and journalists tend to adversely affect the general public's whole idea of light aviation, simply because they misunderstand the subject. One quick trip in a Cessna isn't going to give any journalist a thorough education on how to write about aviation themes in future, but it can go a long way towards preventing him or her going into print with a half baked report maligning small aeroplanes, before first checking on the facts.

A group of eager youngsters who are about to become Young Eagles. Introducing children to flight in a light aircraft can often be a very rewarding experience for the pilot.

If you know a television, press or radio reporter, why not consider inviting him or her to come along with you for a flight? Make sure the aeroplane is looking its neat and tidy best, pick the right weather, and resist the temptation to throw the aeroplane about the skies. Do all you can to give this important passenger as good a first impression of GA as you can. By doing something along these lines you can certainly help dispel, in at least that member of the media, some of the frequent misconceptions that exist about light aviation. You'll then have done your bit to ensure that your latest passenger's reports will be more factual in future, and less biased against small aircraft.

Faint Hearted Flyers

Flying is not a natural part of human life in the way that it is inherent in the lives of most birds, give or take the odd kiwi or penguin. Even in advanced countries like the USA, the UK and other European states, which are constantly being flown over by scheduled services and holiday charter airlines, significant numbers of the population have never left the ground. Many of these people have just never had any occasion to take to the air, but many others have never flown because of inherent anxiety or even downright fear of flying. Some research carried out by the University of Bristol has shown that between 20% to 25% of individuals in Western populations are apprehensive about flying, even in airliners, never mind small two seat or four seat light aircraft. Norwegian researchers have established that, of the people who actually do fly in commercial airliners, some 21% of female passengers are always afraid of flying. The Boeing Company has also gone into this field of research and has concluded that about 17% of the US population is afraid of flying and 24% of all airline travellers experience some feelings of anxiety. They reckon that their customers, the airlines, are losing several millions of dollars of revenue every year because many of the 17% of people who are afraid of flying make a point of avoiding the experience altogether.

Given this background, it is virtually certain that some of the people you fondly imagine would be delighted to have you offer to take them flying will instead be scared stiff at the very idea of going up with you. Don't take it too personally. It is very likely to be because your potential passenger firmly believes that if man had been intended to fly, God would have given him wings. Many people also suffer to some degree from what could clinically be termed a phobia about flying, an irrational, exaggerated fear that is totally out of proportion to the level of danger actually involved. Despite being quite comfortable yourself, sitting in a small, lightly constructed machine supported several thousand feet above the ground by thin air, you perhaps have some phobias of your own. How do you fancy tightrope walking (without a safety net, of course)? Or an afternoon pot holing deep down under the Mendips, perhaps? You might on the other hand prefer dangling at the end of a nylon rope off some vertical cliff-face in the Cuillins of Skye? A weekend adventure camping among the snakes (or spiders) in a jungle clearing then? Or maybe a month long underwater cruise in one of the Royal Navy's Trident submarines? Most of us have some hang ups of our own, so you should never deride a panic stricken passenger. Whatever you do, don't try too hard to cajole him or her into flying with you. You would both almost certainly regret it in the end.

Partner Problems

When the non air minded person involved happens to be the pilot's partner, the situation can be particularly serious. No matter how enthusiastic newly qualified pilots may be, however determined they are to make full use of their PPLs, the fact that their husbands, wives or other close partners constantly refuse to fly with them often makes it only a matter of time before that nice new hard earned PPL ends up lying forlornly in the back of a desk drawer. Thereafter the closest its owner is ever likely to come to piloting again is longingly casting a wistful look at cruising Katanas and passing Pipers. What a waste of a good licence; what a downright shame it is when that sort of thing happens.

Popular Misconceptions

Fear of flying is largely groundless. Statistically, flying is safe. Airliners are safer than little aeroplanes admittedly, but even light aircraft have a pretty good safety record. One of the troubles here is that, as already mentioned, flying tends to get a bad press. Headlines in the media about air show fatalities greatly outnumber reports of the far more numerous air shows that take place, devoid of any mishap. Typical sensational local newspaper stories of perhaps an injury free misjudged landing seldom make mention of the fact that this 'accident' was the first incident of its kind to take place at the local aerodrome for many years. To many non flyers, the mental image of a pilot is a young, physically fit male, possessed of a reckless brand of macho courage and with little sense of danger. (World War 2 flying films do have a lot to answer for.) Not feeling themselves to be in that category, the reluctant passengers simply opt out of anything to do with small aeroplanes.

Luckily, this irrational fear is not insurmountable. Many competent pilots made their first flights with distinctly sweaty palms and dryness of the mouth, yet soon got over that and went on to learn to thoroughly enjoy flying. There is an ancient Chinese belief that to conquer a beast you must first find it beautiful, and there is no doubt that once a person begins to discover the real beauty of flight, then flying ceases to hold the terror it may once have done. Psychologists tell us that not many people are really scared of anything they fully understand. To the lay person, quite how a lump of metal (or plastic or wood) with human beings inside it gets itself up into thin air and, what is more, actually manages to stay up there, seemingly unsupported, remains an incomprehensible mystery. Clear up at least some of that mystery and in many cases you automatically clear up a lot of the anxiety as well. Simple explanations in advance, of what is likely to happen, do usually help to calm nervous passengers in the air too. The facts that engines are noisy on take-off and that banking to turn is standard practice should be spelled out. Passengers should also be forewarned that thermals and turbulence tend to affect light aircraft more than they affect airliners and that the odd bump or lurch doesn't herald the end of life as we know it.

Popular misconceptions concerning light aircraft abound. Many non flyers believe it to be a well known fact that they'll inevitably drop out of the sky if they are so unfortunate as to fly into one of these mysterious phenomena known as 'air pockets'. All your passengers who drive know that if you stall the engine of a car you are left powerless and helpless unless you can get it started again. They have heard that light aircraft can stall too and naturally presume that this is liable to have similar, if not even more disastrous, results. A simple clarification of some such facts of flying (though not a lengthy erudite aerodynamic explanation) can go a long way towards calming unfounded fears. Some people are scared silly about making fools of themselves by being airsick. Often the very fact that they are anxious can aggravate this situation. Even as simple a matter as knowing that there are easily accessible sick bags can reduce tension and make an apprehensive passenger immediately feel better about this. So too can a pilot who is determined to fly smoothly (avoiding steep banks and being gentle whenever changing from climbing to level flight), who tries to keep the passenger interested in what is going on and never attempts to show off his or her skills as an airman (other than by pulling off a greaser of a landing). You may have your own ideas about which phase of flight is the most hazardous, but nothing will ever convince Joe or Jill Public that anything is more dangerous than the landing. To them that is a well known scientific fact. Expect a slight frisson from your passengers as you near that stage of the flight and do your best, when you have any inexperienced passengers on board, to make your landing an especially smooth one.

Reassuring the Anxious

The Bristol University study mentioned earlier, asked a random selection of passengers who were waiting for flights in the Gatwick departure lounge, what aspects of flying they were most anxious about. The 'unnaturalness of flying' and 'fear of falling out of the sky' were equal first. Following these, in order, came 'loss of personal control over the situation', 'take-off', 'landing' and 'instability of the aeroplane'. Among a group of people attending a course specifically designed to help them overcome fear of flying, the main anxiety arousers were similar, together with 'fear of the unknown'. Very few people, according to this study, are unduly worried about mechanical or technical failure of the engine or aircraft. Just the same it does no harm to take any obviously nervous passenger with you as you collect and study the Met forecast, so demonstrating that you also take that aspect of safety seriously. Explain why you are, or are not, filing a flight plan. This is because many people seem to regard flying without filing a flight plan as being hazardous in the extreme, one result of frequent newspaper reports of aircraft accidents which include the ostensibly critical (but usually totally irrelevant) remark that 'the pilot had not filed a flight plan'. As you do the pre flight walk round, explain what you are doing and why you are doing it. For good measure you could point out the contrast between this prudent pilot's procedure and the sloppy technique of the average car driver who is quite happy to launch into a high speed motorway journey without so much as an oil level or tyre pressure check. It is probably also worth mentioning that all aircraft have mandatory servicing, and that components like the engine and instruments are 'lifed' unlike a private car which is all too often simply driven to the stage where one of the rescue organisations has to be called to tow it home. Point out that light aircraft have two ignition systems and (if appropriate) two VHF radios, two fuel pumps, two fuel tanks etc, to provide back up in the unlikely event of any one of these duplicated items happening to fail.

When mentioning the dreaded 'failure' word, you should also mention that even if the engine were to fail up there, this would not mean the whole contraption hurtling straight down to an inevitable crash in the way many non flyers imagine it would. Explain how well a light aircraft can glide and how the one you are flying can, if necessary, be landed safely in almost any reasonably sized agricultural field. Offer to demonstrate what happens if you pull the power off in flight but never force that demonstration on a reluctant passenger. That might make matters worse instead of better.

Stopping Spouses Shivering

For the really reluctant spouse or partner, one of the courses run to help people cope with flying fears is probably worth considering. These are designed primarily for airline passengers but most of them do cover a lot of ground relevant to all flying. 'Fear of Flying' courses are run every few weeks at nine airports around the British Isles including London (Heathrow and Gatwick), Birmingham, Dublin, Glasgow and Manchester International Airports by Aviatours (Charter) Limited. Each lasts for one day, during which participants are given a talk by an experienced airline captain on popular misconceptions about flying, how aircraft stay in the air, why they bank when they turn and what all these odd noise level changes mean. He is also happy to answer questions on topics that seem to worry potential passengers, such as what happens if the plane gets hit by lightning, or an engine fails, or the undercarriage sticks in the up position. After lunch the course is taken over by a psychologist who explains how panic attacks can be coped with, explains that flying phobia, whether genetic or acquired, can be conquered and gradually prepares the students on the course for its third and decisive phase. This is where they are invited to board a Boeing aircraft for a flight to see how they feel about flying after their new insight into what flying is all about. Occasionally some participants fall at this last hurdle and won't leave the departure lounge, but the majority build up enough courage to make the 45 minute flight. During it, the captain explains everything that is going on in a running commentary on each move, bump, whine, and change in attitude or noise level. For others the course was of more limited success, but many who previously were nervous wrecks at the very thought of getting into an aeroplane, have become much more relaxed about the whole business of flying. A course of this nature, including the flight, costs less than £250; no more than a few hours rental of a club aircraft. If it manages to turn a reluctant spouse into a willing passenger that could be money very well spent.

As an alternative, or as a follow up, what the Americans call a 'Pinch hitter' course might also make a good investment. These short courses are designed, not to teach non flyers to become qualified pilots, but to take them to the stage where they would be perfectly capable of getting a light aircraft safely back onto the ground if the pilot were to be incapacitated in flight. And believe it or not, that remote possibility is a source of more refusals to fly in small aeroplanes than you might imagine. No one wants their partner to collapse with a heart attack at any time, but the idea of this happening while you are both up in a small aeroplane that one is piloting can be a pretty terrifying thought. It is not difficult to understand this attitude of mind either. Just imagine how you would feel, abandoned aloft in an aeroplane, not knowing anything at all about how to work that mysterious VHF radio, not having a clue about how to get the aircraft back down onto the ground again, and beginning to see the Angel of Death staring you straight in the face. This is one situation where a little knowledge is not a dangerous thing, but quite the opposite. All it takes to become a Pinch hitter is a couple of hours training with a good instructor, and if that can turn your petrified partner into a keen co pilot it could turn out to be one of the best flying investments you ever made. The Aircraft Owners' and Pilots' Association (AOPA) has a suggested syllabus for a Pinch hitter course and many flying schools and instructors will be happy to take your partner through the short ground school and the couple of hours instruction in the air. That is all that should be necessary to banish this source of worry from your partner's mind and from there on all you have to do is make sure he or she occasionally gets in a bit of practice as a Pinch-hitter. (The term Pinch hitter, incidentally, derives from the American baseball game, where a Pinch hitter is someone who comes on to play as a substitute.)

Collision Hazards

One item that seldom seems to enter the apprehensive passenger's head is the idea that you might bump into another aircraft. We certainly don't want to add yet another worry to those they already have but, as mentioned above, asking passengers to help you keep a good look out makes them feel a useful part of the team and gives them something positive to do during the flight. You should, of course, assure them that the sky is a very big place compared with the restricted space on a roadway and that midair collisions are very rare occurrences indeed.

Had aircraft been developed and used long before cars, what reaction do you imagine an inventor would have received from the general public when he first proposed a new means of transport called an automobile? He would have had to describe it as being rather like a light aircraft with its wings and tail removed. It would travel along narrow bands of asphalt or concrete and would be able to overtake slower automobiles only by steering to miss them by a gap of just a few inches. Oncoming automobiles (with a closing speed of up to around 140 mph) would constantly be missing each other by a similar narrow margin. Directional control to enable the 'pilots' of automobiles to aim for these narrow gaps was to be entirely dependent on the grip being maintained between a few square centimetres of rubber and the asphalt surface.

Seasoned pilots and passengers of light aircraft would probably have laughed him out of court; nobody would be so crazy as to risk their lives in a dangerous and impracticable traffic system like that. As the bumper stickers say, 'I'd rather be flying, it's safer'.

Chapter 2
New Horizons

Bigger... and in Some Ways Better

The first few ventures you fly as a newly qualified pilot, (taking some of your friends for a flight or visiting a new airfield or three) you may well fly in the same type of aircraft as the one you trained in, quite possibly the self-same club or school aeroplane. It will not be long though before you decide it is time to make the change from flying what is essentially a training tool, to piloting something a bit more like a 'going places' aeroplane. You may be bold enough and wealthy enough to head straight up the scale to a higher-power, retractable-undercarriage aircraft, possibly with a constant-speed propeller. More likely though, you will trade the training Tomahawk for a touring Archer, or swap your Cessna 152 for one of those ubiquitous Cessna 172s or Skyhawks. Recently qualified pilots have a tendency to be rather conservative, aeroplane-wise, and often decide to carry on flying types built by the manufacturer they know best.

After your two-seat trainer, what do you choose to fly? If you learned to fly in a Katana like this...

... then when looking for a larger aircraft you might well choose to stay with Diamond aircraft and rent or buy a four-seat DA-40

If you are in the bolder category and are heading straight for a more complex aeroplane, then if you wish you can skip the rest of this Chapter of the book. In Chapter 6 you will find there is a whole section designed to help you adjust to retractable undercarriage aircraft and all the other goodies that usually go with them. For those pilots who would rather make their advance through aeroplane types in more gradual steps, let's look first at what is involved in the move from a basic trainer to one of the simpler types of touring aircraft. This generally means the change from a two seat to a four seat machine and that automatically brings with it decidedly greater importance to the question of weight and balance of the aeroplane. Aircraft like the Cessna 172, Grumman Cheetah, Piper Archer, Diamond DA 40, Cirrus SR 22, Aerospatiale Tampico and many others, are advertised and sold as four seat aircraft but some of them can in fact be used to carry four people within their certified limits of weight and C of G position only if great care is taken. Usually four up is possible only if no baggage is on board or, alternatively, if the fuel tanks are only partially filled. You should therefore never plan on flying this class of aeroplane with four on board to anything approaching its maximum range, without first very carefully checking the all important weight and balance schedules.

You will find these schedules in the aircraft pilot's operating handbook (POH) and having a thorough read-through of this publication is certainly the best way for you to start your conversion from trainer to tourer. Once you have digested the POH for the type you intend flying next, you will probably have a few questions to put to a helpful instructor, or to someone who is more familiar with piloting the type involved. With the answers to your questions committed to memory, head next for quite a few minutes of quiet contemplation sitting on your own in the new cockpit whilst the aeroplane is sitting on the ground. Get yourself familiar with the new positions of things like the trim wheels, fuel cocks, flap levers, seat adjustments, instrument layout and so on. Then look carefully over what is probably a much more comprehensive avionics installation than you had on the trainer. The radios may well work completely differently; there may be a selector panel that is new to you, and a transponder, GPS, VOR or DME perhaps. Have you ever seen that instrument called an EGT gauge before? There is no point whatsoever in paying to hire and fly an aeroplane with any unfamiliar piece of gear in it, until you know what it can do for you and until you are comfortable that you know exactly how to operate it. Get accustomed to entries and exits (normal and emergency) and find out about door and baggage compartment latching. Work through all the checklists for the new aircraft, asking someone if you are unsure of exactly where anything is or how a particular check should be done.

Bigger isn't Always Better

When you actually come to fly the new machine you should be prepared for the touring aircraft's higher cruising speed; it is likely to be around 15 knots faster than its smaller trainer brethren. Remember though that not all performance differences will be improvements. When a four seater is loaded close to maximum permitted weight, you will find that the take-off distance required to clear the nominal 50 foot obstacle is appreciably longer (in the case of the Cessna 172, about 300 feet more than is needed for the 152) and that the sea level rate of climb is poorer. During take-off most pilots graduating from two seat to four seat seat aircraft are quite surprised at the amount of extra right rudder they need to keep straight; this is one result of having a higher horsepower engine turning a larger diameter propeller. Most of the control forces will feel a bit heavier too and you will soon find that trimming the aircraft is even more helpful to you than it was in your trainer. Proper trimming reduces pilot fatigue and makes it easier to maintain accurate heights and headings and to make consistently smooth landings. The main reason behind this change is the higher wing loading of the bigger aircraft. This factor also makes these types more stable in turbulence and somewhat less prone to floating down the runway the way some trainer types tend to do.

If you decide to make your 'upgrade' change to a type of aircraft that is built by a different manufacturer, such as from Katana to Cessna 172 or from Cessna 152 to Grumman Cheetah, you should be prepared for a few additional culture shocks. Your view from the cockpit may be radically altered, for the worse or better, especially whilst in the circuit. As you make your turns, low wings get out of the way to let you see the runway you are heading for, whilst high wings have a nasty habit of hiding the threshold from sight. Gravity fed fuel in high-wing aircraft and the need for electric fuel pumps on low wing designs must be got used to. Also, you must adjust to the narrower main wheel spread of many high wing aircraft, which makes them a little less stable on the ground in windy conditions than most low wing designs.

Knowing your aeroplane thoroughly is essential for safe flying in whichever type of aircraft you may choose to pilot. Making a point of really getting to know the intimate details of each new aircraft you fly is an excellent habit for you to get into when your PPL is still fairly fresh. It is a habit that will make your later transition to more complex types easier, safer and more satisfying for you.

Feel Comfortable Away from the Circuit

One sad, but not infrequent, reason for some pilots losing their enthusiasm for flying is simply the fact that they never pluck up enough courage to venture very far from their home airfield. Doing endless circuits or even slightly extended tours of the immediate neighbourhood does soon begin to pall, not only for you as a pilot but also for any passengers who venture up with you on more than one occasion.

During your training for the PPL you probably spent most of your airborne time fairly close to the airfield and in the local flying area. By the time you got your licence you had become pretty familiar with most of the local landmarks and were reasonably confident of being able to find your way back to base without any difficulties. Your experience of flying elsewhere at that stage was probably no more than a short spell of navigation training plus your dual and solo qualifying cross country flights. You may be one of those pilots who got back to base after flying around that triangular trip with a feeling of some surprise and immense relief that you ever found your way home again. Yet the real purpose of most civil aeroplanes is to convey people and goods expeditiously and safely from one place to another. It rather defeats the object of the exercise if you spend most of your post PPL flying taking yourself from one place right back to that same place again. It is also unfortunately one of the surest ways of guaranteeing the onset of boredom with flying and the probable lapse of a perfectly good PPL.

Even if you do most of your pre-flight planning on a PC you should still always at least draw your track line and turning points on a current aeronautical chart, like this 'half million' with a green line showing the track from Bristol to Welshpool via the VOR at Brecon and Haverfordwest airfield.

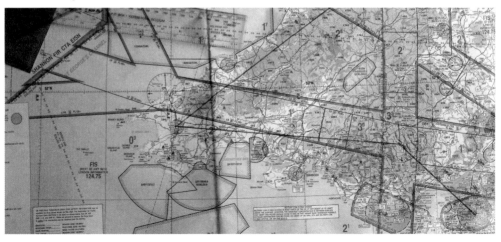

Depending on your attitude of mind, reaching out geographically towards new horizons can seem to be either an exhilarating challenge or an unnecessary risk. But refusal to meet the challenge is also to risk losing through sheer boredom the licence you have worked so hard to earn. There is a corny old (anonymous) quotation about risk that seems to apply here.

'Risk must be taken, because the greatest hazard in life is to risk nothing. The person, who risks nothing, does nothing, has nothing. Only the person who risks is free.'

Flying to faraway places really can be a great experience and, provided you plan and prepare properly for it, the risk of making a fool of yourself by getting lost is really pretty minuscule. A small aeroplane opens up wonderful opportunities for travel to destinations denied to mere ground bound mortals. It is just as easy to fly to offshore islands as it is to drive to neighbouring towns. Crossing the Irish Sea or the English Channel is no longer a major undertaking involving ferry schedules or 'Le Shuttle'. You find many mainland European countries are now within day trip distance of southern England; Ireland is just an hour or so away from northern England or Wales; the Hebrides and northern Isles have become just a couple of hours flying time away from much of Scotland. But to enjoy all these benefits you must first break the mental umbilical cord that seems to tie some pilots to their home airfield.

Keep it Simple to Start With

Gently does it. Don't make your first post PPL cross-country into a major expedition by choosing a hard to find little grass airstrip somewhere at the other end of the country as your destination. That would be as good a way as any of frightening yourself off ever trying anything else. Becoming 'uncertain of your position' (as 'lost' is often euphemistically termed) is not difficult to do for any pilot in the early days, but if you start your cross country flying by being well prepared for an easy trip and work gently up from that point you'll do all right. You should be able, most of the time at least, to avoid that sinking feeling of not being quite sure whether you really are where you think you ought to be. But we have to accept that it does still happen occasionally, even to the best of pilots.

Before even working out a good route, you should check that you know how to operate all the navigational gizmos you have available on the panel. Some flying instructors have an unfortunate habit of explaining little more than the most rudimentary uses of the VOR, DME and ADF during your PPL training. If in doubt seek help from an Instructor or chose an IMC/Radio Navigation course. If there is a GPS (see Chapter 7) in the aircraft kit (or you own one of your own or can borrow one) master how its knobs and buttons work before you take-off. Properly handled, a GPS makes it very, very difficult for a pilot to get thoroughly lost. However, operated without the basic knowledge of their functions and limitations, GPS receivers and moving maps can be downright misleading. Every hour you spend studying the user's manual on the ground, if possible coupled with a bit of practice with the GPS receiver in 'Demo Mode', will be repaid many times over in the air. If you have access to a PC, there are several very useful programs and simulators available (see Chapter 7) which make it easy and inexpensive, to learn how to make the most of VORs, DMEs and ADFs for navigation whether you are flying VFR or IFR.

Many PC flight simulator programs nowadays incorporate good UK scenery which can be reasonably useful as preparation for cross country flights. Even the programmers would hesitate to claim that all their scenery is really true to life, but some of the best of the add on UK and other European scenery for the latest flight simulator programs can be good enough to give a real life VFR pilot a pretty good idea of what to look out for on the approach into a new destination airfield. Cities, motorways and main roads, service stations, coastlines, prominent buildings, lakes, power stations and, of course, aerodromes, all appear tolerably lifelike on the monitor screen. A preliminary PC flight along the planned route can sometimes give a newcomer to VFR navigation in the air a slight sense of 'déjà vu' when the real landmarks actually turn up later, just as expected, outside the windscreen of the aircraft. There is more for you to read about these PC flight simulators in Chapter 7.

Even though the scenery is of lower resolution than in many PC flight simulator programs, it is still easy to recognise where this Bonanza is flying from the curve of the Thames and the Millennium Dome in the background.

Once you have mastered the techniques of using VORs and NDBs, it is a useful insurance to plan your early trips to airfields which have nav aids on or close to them. You may never even tune them in, but it is always comforting to know that they are available should your map reading and dead reckoning happen to hit a snag. With so much of the UK close to the coastline (which really is the easiest visual navigational feature in the world) picking a first destination that lies close to a well defined coastal feature is another suggestion you might consider. As you succeed in finding the first few airfields you aim for, your confidence in your own ability will quickly rise and it will all gradually begin to seem easier. Soon you will be quite happily setting out for insignificant little grass airstrips tucked away in the midst of lots of other similar looking grass fields that aren't airfields and one day you'll very probably find you just cannot identify the one you are looking for at all. Perhaps your planning that time was just a little slipshod?

A well defined stretch of coastline like this is usually an excellent feature to help with map-reading and navigation

Preparing for the Unexpected

All through your pilot training you will have been made very much aware of the fact that aero engines are not infallible and that they do occasionally fail in the air. Your instructor's insistence that you continuously search for fields suitable for forced landings without power, all the exercises you had to do in practice forced landings, and the simulated engine failures sprung on you immediately after take-off, all tend to imprint on your mind the idea that the break down of an aero engine must be an almost everyday occurrence. For some impressionable folk this type of training can have a very inhibiting effect on the flying they are prepared to do after qualifying for their PPLs. In aviation's very early days, engines were notoriously unreliable. Running time between failures was almost measured in flying minutes rather than hours, and the fact that a pilot arrived on schedule at the end of an hour long flight was something to be commented upon.

Nowadays aircraft engines are, by and large, pretty reliable beasts. Those few that do fail in the air have very often given their pilots clear advance warnings that problems were imminent, warnings that the pilot either didn't understand or simply chose to ignore. An engine that has always been easy to start doesn't suddenly become recalcitrant without some reason, possibly mechanical. A sudden increase in oil or fuel consumption, any anomalous readings on gauges for pressure, the cylinder head temperature or exhaust gas temperature, are all things that ought to be investigated by engineers before the aircraft is ever taken into the air again. Unusual mag drops, rough running, misfiring, oily engine cowlings or nacelles can all frequently be signals that something is seriously wrong with the engine's state of health. You should then be looking for expert opinion on the ground rather than risking engine failure in the air.

Nowadays light aircraft engines like this 160hp Lycoming, are generally pretty reliable beasts

Statistically, according to AOPA USA, around 200,000 hours are flown for every forced landing that takes place. (These figures relate to forced landings without power, not the ones that are caused by pilots flying into bad weather or getting hopelessly lost and putting down under power into a field.) There seems to be no reason why the ratio should be all that different in European countries. So, statistically, a PPL qualified pilot flying even a generous total of 200 hours per year, could anticipate having to cope with a forced landing roughly once in every thousand years. But, as Mark Twain put it, *'There are three kinds of lies; lies, damned lies and statistics'*. Concerning forced landings, I am well aware that this quote is true from personal experience, having had to cope with two forced landings during my first 2,000 hours of piloting. One was due to the fracture of a conrod in an ancient, but normally very reliable, seven cylinder Cheetah radial engine. This is one of the few types of engine breakdown that gives the unfortunate pilot no advance warning whatsoever. My second forced landing (virtually without power) was the consequence of the head of a snapped exhaust valve being mangled up inside the cylinder of a Lycoming. I have to admit that particular engine had done its best to let me know that all was not well. It had become tricky to start and wasn't running quite as smoothly as it used to, but foolishly I hadn't interpreted the message it was trying to convey to me. One lives and one learns. The lesson to learn here is that if there is ever any doubt in your mind about the serviceability of an aircraft or its engine, forget any other pressures there may be for you to fly; just don't take the machine into the air. That way, with any luck, you should make a close approach to the statistical 200,000 hours before you have to cope with your first forced landing.

Even if you do happen to draw the short straw and find yourself up in the air one day with a dead engine and a wind milling prop, remember that it isn't by any means the end of the world. If you are flying a fixed undercarriage single engine aircraft you can console yourself with the thought that 95% of all forced landings in these are brought off successfully without any serious injuries or fatalities to the occupants. In single engine retractables, for some reason about 10% of the forced landings do result in serious injuries or deaths, and this figure rises to 25% in the case of twins. Even two engine jet airliners occasionally get involved in forced landings. On one memorable occasion in July 1984 a Boeing 767 ran out of fuel yet was safely landed (without injury to any of the 61 on board) on a disused airfield in Manitoba by its Captain Robert Pearson. As luck would have it, he just happened to be an experienced sailplane pilot.

Common Sense Failure Avoidance

The problem experienced by that Air Canada Boeing (running out of fuel) is in fact one of the most common causes of GA aircraft forced landings. It is also one of the most easily avoided. Even more frustrating are the forced landings that occur due to fuel starvation through the pilot's mismanagement of the fuel system while there is still a perfectly adequate supply of fuel on board. Add to these two causes the engine 'failures' due to pilots who don't apply carburettor heat as soon as necessary when they encounter carburettor icing and you have accounted for over half of all GA forced landings. So if you know how to manage your fuel system, if you make a point of always carrying sufficient fuel for the trip, plus adequate reserves, and if you are able to recognise the symptoms of carb icing and be ready to apply full carb heat whenever these occur, you have already cut your chances of being involved in a forced landing by more than half. About another 10% of all forced landings are caused by fuel contamination, so once again it is in your own hands as the pilot to improve your chances of never being confronted by a forced landing. You should always make a point of checking all the fuel tank and sump drains. If you make sure there is no water or dirt in the fuel, that it is the correct colour for the grade of AVGAS (or MOGAS) that you use and that it has no paraffin smell indicative of AVTUR contamination you will improve your chances. A conventional piston engine will stop immediately pure jet fuel is fed into it, and even a mixture of jet fuel and avgas can cause internal detonation in the cylinders, with consequential risk of major mechanical damage to the engine. In the same way, an engine designed to operate on diesel fuel or JET A1 fuel will not run on AVGAS or MOGAS. Now that increasing numbers of light aircraft are flying on 'diesel' fuel it is more vital than ever to

Now that light aircraft use several different types of fuel (including AVGAS, MOGAS, JET A1 and Diesel) it is especially important that pilots ensure the tanker or pump they are using has the correct fuel for their aircraft.

ensure that piston engine aircraft designed to burn AVGAS or MOGAS are never fed the wrong fuel diet. At one time, many turbocharged piston engine aircraft were prominently marked with the word 'Turbo' somewhere on their flanks and this did tend to mislead some refuellers into filling the tanks with fuel appropriate for gas turbine engines. If any aircraft you fly still carries the dangerous 'T' word, be especially careful when refuelling. or safer still, remove the offending decal or badge altogether. It is always a good idea to have fuel colour coding on wing next to filler cap or the words AVGAS.

If the Worst Comes to the Worst

There remains a statistically tiny possibility that, despite your having done all the correct things to avoid stupid engine failures, you still may be unfortunate enough to encounter an engine with a crankshaft, bearing, conrod, piston or other normally reliable component that lets you down without warning. Is there any way to prepare for such an eventuality, so that you can maximise your chances of getting away with a forced landing with nothing worse to show for the experience than a muddy pair of shoes from walking through a farmer's field? The first thing for you to do, assuming that it isn't an engine failure at low altitude, is to trim the aircraft to its best gliding speed then run through the 'engine failure in flight' checklist. This is one checklist you really ought to commit to memory and rehearse from time to time; the moment just after everything goes quiet is not the time to have to start thumbing through an owner's manual looking for it. If the engine has stopped in a cloud of oil or with a sudden mechanical judder, if the prop has parted company with the crankshaft, or some other obviously terminal failure has occurred (or if you know you really are stupid enough to have run out of fuel) go straight on to the next stage directly and start looking for a landing place. Otherwise check the mag switches, change tanks, try each mag separately, change mixture settings, switch to hot air, use the fuel booster pump if there is one, and follow the rest of that check list. You never know, it might be possible to bring the seemingly dead engine back to life. Once you have completed all this, if time permits and you still have enough altitude to stand a chance of being heard, put out a distress call to enable ATC to alert the search and rescue services for you.

If the engine refuses to restart, where is the best place for you to land? All your practice forced landings were probably aimed at the most suitable looking piece of farmland in the vicinity because that has much better training value than the best place for a forced landing. The really best place is usually an aerodrome if there happens to be one in the vicinity. This does not apply if the emergency you are involved with is an engine failure immediately after take-off. You almost certainly won't make it back to the field you've just left, so don't even try. The only helpful policy to counteract this situation is always to make it a habit to gain as much height as you can as quickly as possible after take-off. If you are high enough and have a GPS receiver with the 'nearest facility' feature, you might want to use it to find out how far, and in which direction, the nearest airfield is. The fairly typical four-seat, 150hp single engine aircraft I usually fly can, at its best glide speed, cover more than seven miles from 4,000 feet with the prop windmilling. Like most light aircraft it will glide even farther if you can stop the prop windmilling, when it produces less drag. It is thus quite often possible to reach and land at an aerodrome lying several miles away from where the engine quits.

Failing that, a disused aerodrome can be a good bet, although you will have to be careful about the hazards which may exist at some of these. The fact that the tarmac or concrete surface of the runways will probably have deteriorated badly, is not of too much importance when you are making an emergency landing, but what looks like an attractive place to put down can have hidden traps for the unwary. Farmers have often erected fences across the old runways to control livestock, and they also have an awkward tendency to store all manner of odd agricultural things, cars and Farmers Markets on or alongside them, things that may not initially be all that obvious from the air. The approaches to disused runways are, of course, no longer inspected to ensure they are free from obstructions, so beware of wires, masts etc that may make a normal approach tricky. If you happen to be involved in making a precautionary landing at a disused airfield, as opposed to a forced landing with a dead engine, you should always try to take the opportunity of having a close look at the approach and the condition of the runway by making a low fly past before you commit yourself to actually landing there. Disused runways in the UK are usually marked with a white diagonal St Andrew's cross at each end, but with the passage of time, these can become difficult to spot from aloft.

A disused aerodrome can often look like an attractive field for a forced landing but beware of agricultural or industrial obstructions to the runways. These abandoned airfields can also make good navigation landmarks in many parts of the world, but in places like East Anglia and Lincolnshire there are so many of them it is very easy to confuse one with another

Failing an Airfield, Try a Farmer's Field

The next best place for an emergency landing is any decent sized flattish field, chosen using the 5 S's (Size, Shape, Surface, Surrounding and Slope). Preferably with any nearby trees or other obstructions at the upwind end (i.e. the far end, when you are landing into wind) where if you do hit them your aircraft will be travelling slowly. I've often heard it argued that a motorway or main road would be better than a field. It would be smoother, pretty level and with outside assistance readily on hand. This is true, up to a point, but hitting a truck head on is not a recipe for success, nor is tangling with lighting standards or those well nigh invisible wires and cables that festoon many roadsides. A nasty aircraft/vehicle coming together could also keep a whole team of lawyers arguing happily for months on end, all at your expense.

You should aim to reach the vicinity of your chosen field with the aircraft clean and with some height to spare. You ought to avoid any rapid or harsh control inputs while trying to reach your chosen landing place, remembering that in hectic manoeuvring the drag effect of hefty aileron, elevator and rudder deflections can lose you as much height as lowering the flaps does. Aim to manoeuvre so you arrive at a marker point representative of the end of a normal downwind leg at 1,000 feet agl, and then use flaps, lower the undercarriage or side slip as necessary to shed any excess height. The goal you are aiming for is to arrive over the threshold, in a controlled condition, but not flying any faster than the normal short-field threshold speed before you contact the surface. The pre landing checks should include closing the main fuel cock, turning off the ignition, pulling back the mixture to idle cut off position. The master switch should be left on until all electrical requirements (radio, flaps, undercarriage and unlocking the door etc) have been dealt with. Whether or not to lower the wheels of a retractable is very much a matter of judgement, depending on the type of surface; if it is rough, a wheels up landing is generally the safer choice for those on board, though not necessarily for the machinery.

Landing as close into wind as possible and using the approach and threshold speeds you have been taught for short field landings is not a bad formula. It minimises your speed relative to the ground and thus the deceleration forces involved. Another rule worth following that will certainly help your chances of walking off unscathed after a forced landing, is to borrow from road driving practice and always wear a shoulder harness when flying. If the forced landing does result in a sharp deceleration, anyone wearing just a lap strap is going to end up like the dummies you see in the slow-motion car accident films. Your body bends in the middle as your torso jerks forward, then, as the lap strap cuts into your spare tyre, your head starts heading for your feet, but is thwarted en route by the instrument panel, which imprints itself onto your face. Luckily, the majority of forced landings do not involve deceleration forces as violent as car crashes, and this actually makes them more survivable for the occupants. Unless you are unlucky enough to fly into something like rocks, a cliff, a big tree or a substantial wall on final approach, your touchdown from controlled flight at normal sink rate and threshold speed should result, even on a rough or sloping surface, in a much gentler stop than the average car to car head on collision. The aeroplane may well shed bits and pieces as it decelerates, but crushing airframe components actually help to cushion occupants and in a single engine aircraft, that solid lump of engine ahead of the cockpit forms a useful battering ram that helps to protect those on board. Remember that the primary objective in a forced landing is to ensure the survival of the occupants. The aeroplane itself is of comparatively minor importance. If all the occupants survive, it is a successful forced landing; if they all survive uninjured, it is an excellent forced landing; if the aircraft also ends up undamaged, and it is a perfect forced landing.

After Landing Actions

Once you are safely down, even though fire is a remote possibility unless fuel tanks are ruptured, it is as well to exit the aircraft quickly. Don't desert it altogether though. Have someone look after it if possible, whilst someone else goes to search for help, the police or a telephone. The aircraft insurance policy may well include a clause saying the aircraft must be safeguarded as far as possible following any forced landing. Some insurers will reimburse reasonable costs incurred in doing this too, so perhaps you could afford to call Group 4 or Securicor after you've informed the police and ATC of your predicament! That settled, you have only to wipe the mud off your shoes and try to hitch a lift back to the airfield.

Keeping Things in Proportion

Expecting the unexpected is a good maxim in flying; it helps you stay one step ahead of the game, which is a much safer place to be than always trying to catch up with a situation. At the same time, though, you must keep things in perspective. Even though a great deal of your instructional time will have been spent on teaching you how to cope with engine failures, most pilots go through their entire flying lives without ever having to put that training into practice. Fear of losing an engine in the air should never be allowed to restrict the amount or the type of flying you do once you have your PPL. Being well prepared to cope with this eventuality if it ever were to happen to you is an excellent thing. Planning all your flying in constant apprehension of such a remote contingency is a different matter entirely. Your chances of winning a major prize in the National Lottery are probably statistically greater than the chances of you ever encountering that sudden ominous silence in the air.

Planning Ahead

Dozens of text books are available which deal in detail with the subject of flight planning. This chapter has not been written to take their place. The idea here is to make a few suggestions about some things you might be forgiven for overlooking in your first few ventures away from home base. Once you have decided where you are going, whether it is a twenty minute trip for a cup of coffee or a month long holiday journey traversing half a continent, make sure your flight bag contains all the maps, charts, frequency information and flight guides needed to cover the route. And in particular, make sure they are all up to date current editions. The same applies if you are using GPS. Make sure its database is an up to date one, and not one that came with the kit when it was bought three or four years ago. Don't get hemmed in by carrying inadequate map cover. The whole route from Retford to Caernarfon, for instance, is on the CAA 1:500,000 chart for Northern England and Northern Ireland. But what if some unforecast nasty low cloud drifts in on you from the north-west whilst you are in the air? Wouldn't it be nice to have the Southern England chart with you too, just in case you feel the need to divert to some cloud free aerodrome lying awkwardly for you just a few miles off the bottom of your Northern chart?

However good the weather may be, always have at least one alternate destination in mind before you set out. And have its landing information, frequencies etc all to hand too. Mark your route clearly on the chart and if you are embarking on a longish trip, sometimes it is worth marking a second 'bad weather' route too, in case perhaps thunderstorms develop or the cloud decides to cover the hills along the route you originally intended to fly. Don't allow controlled airspace to scare you away from the route you would really prefer to fly. Air Traffic Controllers are actually quite human and only if they are really busy will they refuse you entry to any controlled airspace that is open to VFR traffic. It usually helps if your aircraft is transponder equipped. That is

Ensure you have the correct charts with you for the planned flight. These can be CAA or Jeppesen 1:500,000 scale or CAA 1:250,000 scale or their foreign equivalents another piece of equipment (again often skimmed over lightly by PPL instructors) which you really ought to spend some time getting familiar with before you set off on any serious cross country stuff. Naturally, if you always timidly plan your routes so they go around any CTR, MATZ or TMA and so never have to talk to ATC or ask for clearance through their bit of airspace, you'll never find out how co-operative they can be. Nobody will be very co-operative however if you disregard the regulations concerning any Airways, Prohibited, Restricted and Danger Areas, parachuting and gliding sites, active ATZs and instrument approach tracks/paths etc. Check your chart for these and other kindred restrictions and obstructions. It is always worth bearing in mind the existence of Danger Area crossing and advisory services. You don't have to look any farther than the bottom of your CAA half-million charts to find out about the DACS and DAAIS. Make use of them.

Cross Country Should be Fun

Remember too that you are now flying for pleasure. There is nothing in any section of the Air Navigation Order or the Rules of the Air that says you must always fly the direct route from A to B. If there is a historic castle or a motor racing circuit, nudist colony, chalk hill figure, cathedral or even perhaps a spectacular bit of cliff scenery that might interest you or your passengers, why not go and see it? Take your camera along, enjoy your flight. The world is full of sights and spectacles denied to ordinary groundlings but which look superb when seen from aloft. Don't become so fascinated with the scenery below that you forget to keep a good look out for other aircraft though. You may not be the only pilot having a look see at the Humber Bridge or the Old Man of Hoy that afternoon. And so far as that racing circuit is concerned; if it is active remember your minimum height rules for flying in the vicinity of crowds.

On a cross country flight you can often increase your enjoyment by diverting a little from the direct track so you and your passengers can see interesting aerial views of stately homes, like this one, or other attractions

Flight Plans

There is of course, the other type of Flight Plan, that official piece of paper CA48/RAF F2919 (and its equivalents as issued by foreign aviation authorities). For some obscure reason there are quite a few PPL pilots I know who have a horror of these FPLs. I am sure it is sometimes more the worry about having to complete one of these forms correctly that dissuades them from going abroad, rather than any worries they may have about flying across a stretch of salt water. In practice, as soon as you have done the job a couple of times, filing a VFR flight plan becomes simplicity itself. In some countries, such as Belgium, Denmark and Switzerland, so many private VFR flights cross international borders that almost every private pilot is accustomed to completing Flight Plans regularly for most of his or her flights. In this country, so far as VFR flights in aircraft with a maximum take-off weight which does not exceed 5,700 kg it is mandatory to complete a Flight Plan only for flights to or from the UK which will cross the UK FIR boundary. (Flights within the Scottish and London Upper Information Region (UIR) also require FPLs but since the UIR has its base at Flight Level 245, this is highly unlikely to concern many readers of this book.) Any VFR flight within Class D airspace control zones or control areas also requires a flight plan but it is perfectly acceptable to comply with this requirement simply by passing details of the flight to the appropriate ATC unit by radio while you are in the air.

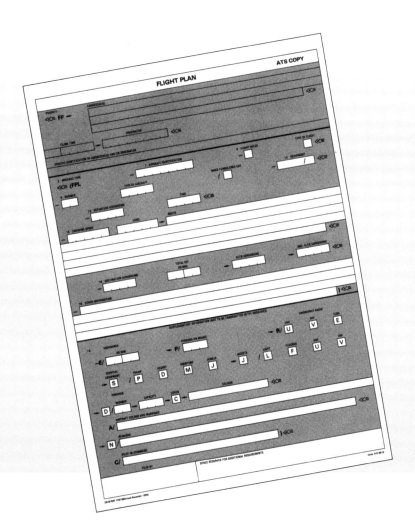

To File or Not to File?

There are other occasions when it is advisable to file a FPL even though there is no mandatory requirement for you to do so. Common sense should tell you when. Sensible hill walkers and mountaineers leave details of their planned route with some responsible person before they head for the mountains, so that if they don't get back to civilization as planned, somebody has at least a rough idea of where to start searching for them. Similarly, sensible flyers don't set out to cross inhospitable terrain (mountains, water, wilderness or desert) without filing a flight plan, for precisely the same reasons. Finally, there is nothing to prevent a pilot from filing a Flight Plan at his or her own discretion for any flight. Always remember to close the FPL if landing at a no-controlled airfield.

Completing the form is not difficult and there are many leaflets, posters and books to help any pilot who is new to the job to learn the basic steps involved. If in doubt, get hold of the CAA's General Aviation Safety Sense Leaflet 20 which clearly shows you how.

Flying Vacations

Possibly not the first summer after you get your PPL, but sometime not too long after that, you are quite likely to begin mulling over the notion of combining your annual holiday with some flying. There are certainly a few complications involved, but none of these is insurmountable and you shouldn't let them put you off what can turn out to be an excellent way of making good use of your licence. Most clubs, and many groups, ask for a certain minimum number of flying hours per day to justify doing without their machine for a period, but provided the figure asked for is not unreasonable, it should equate with what you intend doing anyway. If it doesn't, you probably haven't planned your holiday properly to ensure that it really justifies your use of the aeroplane in the first place.

There are many marvellous flying holiday destinations within the UK, but many pilots plan their first flying vacation for places that are generally reputed (but alas, don't always turn out to be) warmer and sunnier than Britain. France is undoubtedly the favourite destination for British pilots but Spain has many aficionados too, as have Belgium, the Netherlands, Germany and, more recently, some of the eastern European countries. Before you set out for any such destination, you must get acquainted with all the differences that exist between the UK flying regulations that you know and love, and the VFR rules of the country you are heading for and of all the others whose airspace you are likely to be passing through. Europe is much more unified than it used to be but despite JAA and all the other international bodies, each State's aviation authority is still tending to hang on to their own very different sets of VFR rules. This may well change within the next few years but meantime these variations still affect such things as: the UK's Quadrantal Rule (unknown elsewhere in Europe where the semicircular rule largely takes its place); circuit joining procedures; night flying regulations; SVFR limits and VFR in airways (not by any means always forbidden as it is in UK airspace). More detailed information on some of these matters is contained in Chapter 4 of this book under 'Other Countries; Other Customs'. Even the language used by ATC in some places can be foreign to you. Despite English being the language of international aviation, many French and German aerodromes (especially the smaller ones) often use their native tongues for VHF transmissions. Fortunately, however, at many of these airfields the controller can also muster up enough English to cope with pilots unable to speak his or her language.

Don't let yourself be deterred from going because of these differences. There would be little point in bothering to fly abroad at all if everything there were to be precisely the same as it is at home. Just be prepared and learn as much as possible about the variations to expect before you get there. AFE and Pooley's have some useful information in their European Guides, as has Jeppesen, and all the up-to-date facts are to be found in the AIPs for the countries concerned some of which are now accessible on the Internet. If all of this seems to be rather too much to master straight away, you could make a simpler start by trying an 'overseas' flying holiday across the water to the Isle of Man, Guernsey, Mull or Orkney perhaps. Save up all those other lovely island airfields like Belle Isle, Texel, Sylt or Corsica for later, once you have

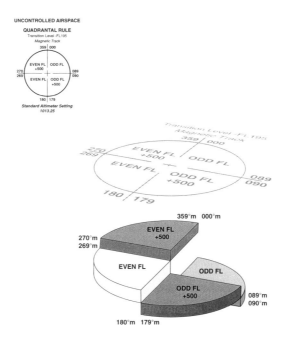

The Quadrantal Rule (Transition altitude to FL195)

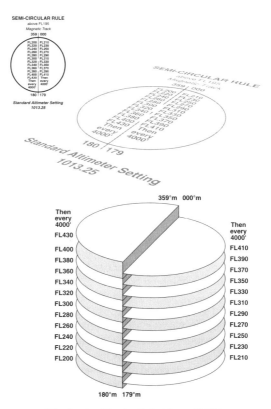

The Semi – Circular Rule (above FL195)

had time to get all the facts together. One useful way of preparing for a trip like this is to read about other pilots' experiences on similar ventures. Pilot magazine, Flyer, Light Aviation and Today's Pilot for example publish many reports on foreign destinations and copies of many of the relevant back numbers are usually available.

Fly While Abroad Without Flying Yourself There

A slight variation on the self-piloted flying holiday theme is well worth considering. This consists of travelling first by airline or surface transport and then renting an aircraft at your destination. Usually, outside of Europe, it is necessary to obtain a local validation of your JAA PPL. Except in a few countries this presents no great problem, other than perhaps swotting up enough about local air law to pass a written or oral test. In the case of the United States, an FAA Airman's Licence can be obtained on the strength of your JAA PPL before you leave the UK, but before you can legally use this on an American N-registered aircraft you first must pass the FAA's Biennial Flight Review. Also, ever since 9/11, more restrictions have been introduced concerning aliens requiring clearance before flying the United States. See www.faa.gov for latest information. With the appropriate formalities for the country concerned behind you, all that remains for you to do is to convince a QFI at a club or school that you can actually fly the machine you want to rent. Then for a few dollars more (or Euros, Swiss francs or what have you) you have a whole new sky to explore. I have enjoyed renting aircraft for vacations like this in many countries including Italy, France, Sweden, the United States, Canada and New Zealand. For the relatively little amount of advance preparation involved, this type of flying can bring an immense amount of pleasure and it often enormously extends the horizons of a holiday in foreign parts, not just for the pilot but for the whole family.

Flying an aeroplane with a foreign registration like this is becoming easier throughout Europe and really presents very little problem for British pilots in many other countries such as the USA, South Africa, New Zealand etc

Navigation Know How

Psychologists claim that very few people are really ever afraid of anything they thoroughly understand. It is awareness of the unknown that causes a great deal of anxiety. If you are just the tiniest bit afraid of getting lost should you venture into the air outside the local area, this is possibly caused by an instinctive feeling that you don't yet know enough about navigation. Navigation is a vast subject and one about which most sensible pilots continue to increase their knowledge all through their flying lives. One paramount rule for an inexperienced pilot is always to plan carefully ahead. Another is to be ready to admit it if, despite all your planning, things don't work out as you had expected. Should you begin to get that uneasy feeling that you may not actually be quite where you think you ought to be, follow a sensible routine. Firstly, note down the present time, the last positive pinpoint you identified and work out how far you should be from there. Check that the Directional Indicator (DI) still agrees with the compass. When searching the chart for where you might be. Remember Time – Map – Ground. Check the timings on your PLOG, refer to your map for expected position. Look out of the window to confirm position. And while you are looking for some distinctive coast, railway, motorway, river or the like, you should try to maintain both your route plan heading and your good look out for other aircraft.

These days most pilots have another alternative. Although it is still not approved for use as a primary means of navigation in the air, if you have a GPS receiver on board and you know how to work the thing, this will more often than not be able to tell you very precisely where you are. But if, despite that, you still get lost, then you must tell someone. Don't wait until the fuel runs low or darkness becomes imminent; that simply compounds the difficulties for everyone concerned. Transmit to whichever ground station you have been working and tell them quite clearly that you are lost. There is no point in talking round the situation. This is no time for false pride. You need assistance, and you should make that fact quite plain to whichever ground station you contact that you really do. If you can get no reply from the station you were last talking to, go straight onto the Emergency frequency 121.50MHz and make a PAN call.

Preventing yourself from getting lost is of course much better than any cure such as this. As already mentioned, one of the best safeguards is always to be equipped with the correct charts for the job. Even if you have the very latest in electronic moving map GPS gizmos on board these can and sometimes do break down, batteries can run flat and their programs can be corrupted much more easily than a good old fashioned paper chart. Old fashioned charts perhaps but not old, please; charts go out of date (just as GPS moving-map databases do) and the only one worth having on board is the latest, current issue. A couple of new UK half-million charts to cover any route you are planning to fly will cost you the equivalent of about 20 minutes flying time in a typical four seat single. They could well save you considerably more than 20 minutes of aimlessly wandering around in the air looking for where you are and becoming more and more confused because the chart you are trying to use is out of date. It is also against the law, incidentally, to fly without having all the charts you need for your flight and for any diversion you might have to make.

Which Chart?

Most purposes in typical light aircraft are best served by the standard ICAO 1:500,000 ('half million') scale charts issued by the CAA, but for more detailed information about the countryside you are flying over, there is also a useful 1:250,000 ('quarter million') scale series available. It is not, however, obligatory to use the CAA published charts. Jeppesen have an excellent series designed for the VFR pilot who uses GPS, but which are equally useful to the pilot who has no access to satellite navigation. These charts have the advantage that all the cartographical detail, map symbols and the whole presentation are the same for all countries in Europe. It can sometimes get a bit confusing if you have to switch from the UK version of the ICAO chart, with which you have become familiar, to a French or perhaps a German equivalent. You are liable to find that spot heights and contours may sometimes be given in metres instead of feet; the symbol for a glider airfield is totally different; the colours used to indicate controlled airspace, airways and danger areas are perhaps based on a convention that is strange to you. In the early days of flying pilots did all their navigation with the aid of maps out of school atlases and motoring maps, there being nothing else available. With no information to add to these, other than the location of aerodromes, in those far off days this was reasonably satisfactory. Nowadays however (although I do know some French and Belgian pilots who still do most of their aerial navigation with the aid of nothing more than marked-up Michelin road maps) up to date charts produced specifically for aviation really are essentials for safe flying.

The financial equivalent of about another twenty minutes of flying time will get you a good book you should take along with you too; one or other of the VFR flight guides that are now available. 'Never fly without your Pooleys' has been a good advertising maxim for many years now, but if you prefer the modern layout and content of AFE's UK VFR Flight Guide or perhaps a Jeppesen manual or Lockyear's Guide to farm strips (or one of the IFR guides such as Aerad or Jeppesen) then the choice is entirely yours. In general my advice would be to pick a VFR guide which has an amendment service that allows you to keep it up to date throughout its year of validity. Like charts (and GPS moving map databases) an out-of-date flight guide can cause a lot of confusion when frequencies have changed, runways been closed, nav aids moved, or any of the many other changes which constantly plague aviation and which may have taken place since your source was last updated.

Typical of the range of Flight Guides available for VFR flying in UK are these; Lockyear's Farm Strip Guide, the AFE UK VFR Flight Guide and Pooley's Flight Guide

Getting all this equipment ready for the flight involves you in quite a few preparatory steps. If the guide book is of the loose leaf variety it is sometimes useful to extract those pages likely to be most relevant and to keep them ready for use, perhaps in a transparent plastic pocket loose leaf book. After the flight, don't forget to put these pages back in their correct order so you can find them again easily next time you need them for another expedition. Concerning the aeronautical charts themselves, you should exterminate all evidence of your earlier flights by erasing the lines relating to them. If you don't, it is all too easy when you are busy in the cockpit for your eye to pick out the wrong line (one left over from an earlier flight) and this is almost guaranteed to cause a fine old muddle in your mind as you try to sort things out again. Even such a small thing as folding the charts in a suitable manner before take-off, so that the whole length of your track line is going to be easy to see, is well worthwhile. Wrestling in the confines of a small cockpit with sheets of paper up to four feet square is something a pilot can well do without.

Now You See It

Only experience will tell you which of the features on a chart make good waypoints and landmarks and which don't. The difference between good and bad features also varies, depending very much on where you happen to be flying. A motorway may well be a prominent feature in some parts of Scotland, but throughout industrial areas of Germany for example, there are simply so many Autobahns around the place that the poor pilot is hard pressed to tell one from another. Big lakes or forests can be good landmarks in many parts of England but over large tracts of Sweden or Finland, for example, it is extremely tricky to tell these apart. Middle sized towns are, in general, reasonable pinpoints, often positively identifiable from a quick study of the angles at which roads and railways enter and leave them, but large cities and conurbations are pretty useless. With these you also have to remember legal limits about the minimum heights you are allowed to overfly them.

Lakes and forests can be good landmarks in some parts of the world, but not in others.

Often conspicuous from the air are aerodromes, disused as well as active. But beware; in some parts of the world (Eastern England in particular) there are so many disused airfields dating from WW2 that they can easily be confused, unless some other distinctive feature close to them ensures positive identification. Grass airfields too often look much more prominent on the chart than they do in the countryside below. Finally, please be careful about using any active aerodrome as a pinpoint, since they are all liable to be busy with other aircraft flying in their vicinity. Sometimes aerodromes have specified Visual Reference Points (VRPs) to help ATC route VFR aircraft into or across controlled airspace and aerodromes with instrument approaches outside controlled airspace. Normal practice is for ATC to ask you to 'report VRP such and such' but it is not necessary actually to overfly the VRP. They will generally be quite happy to hear you report '2nm east abeam so and so VRP' and this can help avoid congestion and collision risk actually over these VRPs. On the other hand, if asked to enter or leave a CTR via a specified entry/exit point you are expected to identify that point on your chart and to overfly it.

Avoid Elementary Errors

Having finished your pre-flight planning, ensured all the charts and documents are accessible in the cockpit (and legible) and included as part of your pre flight inspection the removal of all dust, flies and streaks from the windshield (to give yourself a fighting chance of actually seeing some of the landmarks you have chosen to use) you are finally ready to get airborne. It is quite surprising how often inexperienced pilots (and even one or two pilots who certainly don't come into this category) come unstuck in their navigation at this early stage. A DI that hasn't been correctly aligned with the magnetic compass can oh so easily lead an unwary pilot off in an entirely wrong direction. So can the dyslexic type confusion between steering 030 and 300 on the DI. Tracks of 130 and 310 have also been known to get crossed in pilots' minds and map reading. More than once, VFR pilots have been known to set off, perfectly happily following a nice prominent line feature like the M1 motorway or the river Rhine for quite long distances, before it dawns on them that they have been following it in the wrong direction! You really should always do an early check of compass, direction of the sun (assuming you can see it) and an unmistakable landmark, to make sure that sort of thing isn't happening to you. And concerning the DI, never forget that it precesses (wanders off) in the course of a flight and should always be checked and re-aligned if necessary as part of the regular 10 to 15 minute FREDA checks, (Fuel; Radio; Engine Instruments; DI; Altimeter).

RT Unease

During your training for the PPL you will have learned enough about the basics of how to use an aircraft radio to pass the radiotelephony exam. Your instructor will also have introduced you to most of the standard radio procedures you needed to use for flying in your home airfield environment. If you did your training at a major airport, complete with Ground, Tower, Approach and Radar frequencies for you to cope with, and with controlled airspace around it, then you probably gained sufficient familiarity with your VHF radio to enable you to do most of your future VFR flying radio work without a problem. You will certainly have had a heavier cockpit workload during your training than a pilot who was brought up to PPL standard at a quiet little airfield with no more than perhaps a Flight Information Service (Information) or an Aerodrome Air/Ground Communications Service (Radio). However, you will reap the benefit of this radio experience as soon as you start venturing farther from home in your PPL flying. If, on the other hand, you are one of those pilots who while a student seldom did more on the radio than talk to the local airfield information service, you may well soon find yourself joining the sad ranks of the many PPL pilots who would do almost anything rather than get involved with having to talk to strange Air Traffic Controllers. And that inhibition can seriously cramp your style as a pilot, especially in a country like the UK where so much of the airspace is chock a block with CTRs, TMAs, MATZs, radar services and the like.

For instance, I know of pilots who, faced with a south/north trip up England, refuse to go anywhere near the east coast for the simple reason that they have heard it is covered with terrible things called LARS (Lower Airspace Radar Services). Since this would mean their having to communicate with fast-talking military controllers they head instead for a complex route through the Midlands or west coast, carefully steering around the Birmingham and East Midlands airspace, or creeping along the Manchester Low Level Corridor and avoiding like the plague any airspace where someone might want to talk to them. Unfortunately, these pilots have missed the whole point about ATC and RT. Radiotelephony is designed to allow pilots and ground personnel to communicate with each other, and its primary purpose is to assist the safe and expeditious operation of aircraft. Whilst it is perfectly legal (and often very pleasant) to fly in much of the open airspace over many countries without even switching on your VHF radio, it is pretty dumb not to make full use of RT when it can make your flight so much safer and significantly easier.

Shyness about transmitting on VHF is perhaps understandable and even forgivable in the very early days of pilot training, but a good instructor should ensure that confidence has replaced this resistance long before any student is let loose as a qualified private pilot. If not, however, all is not lost. We have ways of making you talk, however self conscious you may initially feel about it.

Don't Be Shy

Learning the correct phraseology to use is important for two reasons. The first reason is simply for flight safety, to ensure that you transmit in such a way that confusion or misunderstandings do not occur. The second reason is simply to help make you feel you are not a little outsider in the great big world of aviation airwaves. The basic phraseology is laid down clearly in the CAA's Radiotelephony Manual (CAP 413) but if you find that difficult to digest it is always possible to assimilate RT technique through your ears. Not just while you are in the air, but also at home or elsewhere. It is easy to immerse yourself from time to time in the babble of air traffic communications simply by tuning in an appropriate frequency on a VHF band receiver. If you can afford a VHF transceiver (see Chapter 7) so much the better, but simple air band receivers and scanners which are perfectly suitable for this type of listening in are available at prices from as little as £25 upwards. By listening to the professionals' patter you soon get a better 'feel' for what is expected from you as a pilot and you become less likely to make yourself feel awkward or to annoy others on the frequency. Nor will you then be so liable to take up valuable air time unnecessarily the way one notorious pilot did who used to sign off his transmissions with something like 'Piper Warrior Golf Bravo Bravo Lima Tango message received, roger, wilco, over and out, many thanks for all your assistance, and good evening Sir.'

Eavesdropping like this on professional pilots as well as amateurs also helps you to anticipate what ATC is likely to say next and what response you will be expected to come up with. You will also hear from time to time the well-worn phrase 'say again', which is one that you should bear very much in mind. Any time you are left in any way uncertain of what the message is that ATC has just directed to you, don't guess, don't ignore it, don't assume anything, just transmit 'Say again' until you are sure of the meaning of the message.

On the other hand, you will also hear a lot on the RT that does not conform to CAP 413 standards. There are times when informality creeps into RT, times when you can get away with little chats, but until you get the 'feel' for it, you are better to avoid the informality you will sometimes hear from some professional pilots as you listen in on the VHF air band. Once you get into RT practice you will begin to recognise the circumstances when it may be permissible to diverge slightly from the standard phraseology. Don't try to copy the laid back style of some airline captains, don't intersperse your call with lots of 'ums' and 'ahs' and 'ers'. Think what you are going to say before you press the transmit button and then say it distinctly and not too quickly. That way everyone listening will probably know you are a relatively new PPL pilot, but what the hell; the people who need to know will understand exactly what they need to know, which is the whole point of the exercise. You will find that ATC are your friends, and ATC with radar can at times be the pilot's best friend of all.

A hand-held transceiver like this, or a less expensive air band scanner helps pilots assimilate what good R/T sounds like.

What advantages does competence in use of the radio bring for you? Many. Psychologically you feel better, not having a small corner of this piloting business that you are uncertain about always niggling away at the back of your mind. Practically, you can now plan cross country flights without the constraint of trying to avoid having to talk to anyone you don't know. You still won't know who you are talking to, except as a code name like 'Littlefield Radio' or 'Le Touquet Approach', but you will know how to talk to them and how to get them to help you with your flying.

Know What is on Offer

It certainly pays for you to get to know all the different types of service ATC can give you.

Outside of controlled airspace, in Class G or Class F (known as open FIR), it is not mandatory for a pilot to be in receipt of an air traffic service; pilots are solely responsible for collision avoidance and terrain/obstacle clearance.

In the UK there are four distinct services: **Basic Service:** The Controller/FISO will pass information necessary for the safe and efficient flight, this includes weather, changes of serviceability of facilities, conditions at aerodromes and general activity information within a units area of responsibility. It is not necessary to have radar to provide this service. This service is available under any flight rules or meteorological conditions; however a basic service is not appropriate for flight in IMC when other services are available. Controllers may positively identify an aircraft which require the allocation of a squawk. However this does not imply that an increased level of service has been provided. Pilots should not expect any traffic information from a Controller/FISO as they are under no obligation to do so outside an ATZ, and due to higher priority given to other tasks might not monitor traffic receiving a basic service for significant periods. Consequently pilots must maintain adequate look out at all times to avoid other airspace users. A pilot who considers that he requires specific traffic information should request a traffic service. Controller/FISO with positive information indicating that a definite risk of collision exists may pass an appropriate warning to the pilot. Pilots remain responsible for terrain clearance and collision avoidance at all times.

Traffic Service: A Traffic service provides the pilot with radar derived traffic information on conflicting aircraft, no deconfliction advice is passed and the pilot is responsible for collision avoidance. This service can only be provided by a Controller using an ATC radar system. Traffic Service is available under any flight service and/or meteorological conditions. However, a Traffic Service might not be appropriate for flights in IMC when other services are available. Aircraft must be identified for a traffic service to be provided. In order to identify an aircraft, a Controller may need to issue a Squawk or turning instructions to the pilot. If track identity is lost the Controller will attempt to re-establish identity as soon as practicable. Controllers shall pass information on conflicting traffic that they anticipate that will pass within 3nm and 3000ft. Deconfliction advice will not be passed. Controllers shall update the traffic information if it continues to constitute a definite hazard or if requested by the pilot. Traffic information should be passed before the confliction traffic is within 5nm in order to give the pilot sufficient time to visually acquire the conflicting traffic and take the appropriate action. There may be situations where traffic information is provided late or not at all due to various reasons. Consequently pilots must maintain an adequate visual look out at all times. Pilots are responsible for collision avoidance at all times whether traffic information is passed or not. A Controller will not offer deconfliction advice to a pilot in receipt of a traffic service. If a pilot requires deconfliction advice he shall request a deconfliction service Traffic Service is available at all levels subject to the use of the radar in use at the ATC unit. Consequently the service may be provided below ATC terrain safe levels and pilots are responsible for terrain and obstacle clearance at all times. Pilots intending to fly or descend below ATC terrain safe levels will be issued, with a terrain reminder by the Controller. A pilot may operate under his own navigation or a Controller may provide headings for positioning, sequencing or navigation assistance. A pilot shall not change general route manoeuvring area, or Controller allocated heading without permission. Controllers will only allocate headings when the aircraft is at or above the ATC Terrain Safe Level unless the pilot requests such a heading. Pilots may select their own operating levels or be allocated a level by the controller. A pilot shall not change a level band without permission.

Deconfliction Service: A Deconfliction Service provides the pilot with traffic information and deconfliction advice on confliction aircraft. However the avoidance of other aircraft is ultimately the pilot's responsibility. A deconfliction service can only be provided by a controller using an ATC radar system. The service is available under any flight rules or meteorological conditions. Controllers will expect the pilot to accept headings or levels that may require flight in IMC. Pilots do not require deconfliction advice or deconfliction minima to be applied, should not request a Deconfliction service. Aircraft must be identified for a Deconfliction service to be provided. In order to identify an aircraft, a Controller may need to issue a Squawk or turning instructions to the pilot. If track identity is lost the Controller will attempt to re-establish identity as soon as practicable. Controllers may pass traffic information on participating and co-ordinated de-conflicted traffic that may be of relevance to the pilot. Controllers shall provide traffic information on conflicting traffic and advise necessary to achieve separation. However high Controller work load or RT loading or unpredictable manoeuvres by other aircraft mean that the deconfliction minima may not be achieved. The pilot may decide not to act upon the controllers advice, in which case he must inform the controller and accept responsibility for any deconfliction actions that may be required. Controllers may continue to pass traffic information if they consider it constitutes a definite hazard. A Deconfliction service will only be provided to aircraft operating at or above the ATC units Terrain Safe Level unless it is on departure from an aerodrome. During departure and on instrument approach procedures below the general ATC Terrain Safe Level a Controller will pass traffic information without deconfliction advise. If the pilot requests deconfliction or that a controller considers that a definite risk of collision exists, then deconfliction advice will be passed. In such situations the deconfliction advice will be aimed at ensuring that a collision does not occur rather than to achieve planned deconfliction minima. Pilots shall not change heading or level without permission unless safety is likely to be compromised. When a heading or level instruction is provided then the Controller will expect the pilot to comply unless other wise advised.

Procedural Service: A Procedural Service is a non radar service in which instructions are provided to achieve deconfliction minima in receipt or a procedural service from the same controller. The avoidance of other aircraft is the pilots responsibility. The service shall only be provided by controllers at ATC units with CAA approval to provide the service. Controllers at ATC units without radar may routinely apply procedural service to aircraft conducting IFR arrival or departure procedures without the need to elicit the pilots requirements. A Procedural Service is available under any flight rules and meteorological conditions. Controllers will expect the pilot to accept radial, track, level and time allocations that may require flight in IMC. Pilots that do not require deconfliction advice should not request a procedural service. Under a procedural service high reliance is placed on the pilots ability to follow instructions. Therefore in a high controller work load and/or where

airspace is limited controllers may not be able to provide a Procedural Service to a pilot who is flying by visual references. Aircraft do not need to be identified however controllers may allocate a Squawk to improve the awareness of other controllers. Pilots should not assume that a radar service is being provided when a Squawk is used. The Controller will pass traffic information on those aircraft to which he is providing a Basic Service and other flights of which he has been informed of by another ATC units. The pilot remains responsible for collision avoidance at all times. Controllers shall pass deconfliction instructions by allocating, radials, tracks and time restrictions or use pilots position reports to achieve the planned deconfliction minima form other aircraft receiving a procedural service. The deconfliction minima are: 1000 feet vertical; or 500ft vertically where levels are allocated in accordance with the quadrantal rules; nor approved lateral and longitudinal criteria. Deconfliction advice cannot be provided against unknown aircraft and high controller workload may mean that deconfliction minima may not always be achieved. Pilots may encounter conflicting aircraft about which neither traffic information nor deconfliction advice has been provided. The adequacy of ATC deconfliction advice relies on compliance by pilots and as this is a non-radar service,

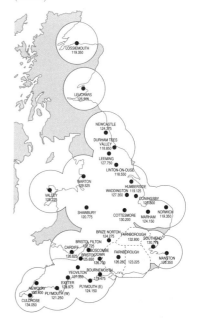

Lower Airspace Radar Services Map (LARS)

controllers are unable to recognise when pilot reports are inaccurate or incorrect. A procedural service is available at all levels and the pilot remains responsible for terrain clearance. Controllers will remind pilots wishing to operate below ATC Terrain Safe Levels of their responsibilities and the relevant Terrain Safe Level. Pilots hall not change level without first obtaining permission.

One of the useful services available to you whilst flying in the 'Open FIR' (that is outside controlled airspace) is the Lower Airspace Radar Service (LARS) , which is a service offering pilots either deconfliction or traffic service. As is the case with other ATC units, it is up to you as pilot to contact them first and ask for whichever type of service it is that you require. Most controllers are very cooperative and friendly men and women, but they aren't psychic, so they can't read your mind to find out what it is you want from them. (Actually, they will generally try to provide the best service available to you at the time if you fail to tell them precisely what you want. Generous people, aren't they?) You can also make use of the MATZ crossing service, Danger Area Activity Information Service (DAAIS) and Danger Area Crossing Service (DACS). It is well worth while getting to know all the various forms of help available to you and the CAA has published an excellent Safety Sense leaflet on the subject (No 8) 'Air Traffic Services Outside Controlled Airspace'.

Sometimes a student pilot gets to the end of his or her training with the false impression that the folk in the control tower think they are some kind of superior beings. Their main purpose in life sometimes appears to have been to make things difficult for pilots, especially pilots learning to fly light aircraft. They keep you waiting on the ground at holding points while the bill for flying mounts up by the minute; they force you to extend your downwind leg just as you thought you had the circuit working out nicely or, even worse, they make you do some orbits to the left to let instrument traffic land ahead of you. Most of them demand specific information from you before they let you fly through 'their' bit of the sky. But the plain fact is that they are there to provide a service, just as much to you as to any other airspace users. Any time you need it, make sure you know how to make full use of it.

Flying a small aeroplane in radio silence through uncluttered skies on a fine clear sunny day can be idyllic, reminiscent of the good old days of flying in the interwar years, but to get the full benefit out of a light aircraft as a means of getting from one place to another these days all pilots really have to be competent and relaxed in their use of VHF radiotelegraphy.

The folk in the control tower aren't some kind of superior beings; they are just ordinary men and women doing their vital job of helping pilots and ensuring air safety

Chapter 3

Weather Factors

Know Your Limitations

Many student pilots find meteorology far and away the most complicated subject that they have to study for their PPL examination. On the other hand many also find it fascinating to learn to understand, perhaps for the first time in their lives, something about weather systems, anticyclones, warm fronts and the like. Weather has always been a feature of our lives of course, an inevitable topic of conversation and something that affects our work, and possibly our hobbies and holidays. It certainly is going to affect every PPL pilot's hobby of flying because it is no exaggeration to say that for every pilot, weather really can be a matter of life and death.

It is an unfortunate fact that weather is involved as a main or contributory factor in a very high proportion of all GA accidents. People continue to have accidents, either because the pilot doesn't understand enough about meteorology to interpret aviation weather data correctly, or because he or she understands it but fails to correlate it sensibly with his or her flying ability, or simply because the pilot foolishly opts to press on, deliberately ignoring an adverse forecast of conditions which are likely to be outside his or her limitations. It is crass stupidity for any pilot to pretend to understand a met report, or the print out of an aerodrome forecast, if you have only the vaguest idea of what '22005KT 2500 BKN005 OVC010' and so on, actually means. You owe it to yourself, never mind to your unsuspecting passengers, to keep on top of this vital subject. And it is bordering on criminal if you make a wilful decision to fly into conditions you know are likely to be beyond you. Yet pilots keep on doing these idiotic things, often getting away with it admittedly, but sometimes sadly adding to the weather related aviation accident statistics.

Thunderclouds are weather phenomena that are always best given a wide berth by pilots of all types of aircraft

Why do pilots do it? The reasons are numerous, but none amounts to anything approaching a valid excuse for risking your own and your passengers' necks in the one sided contest of you against the ruthless and powerful forces of adverse weather. Sometimes it is a matter of cash. To abandon the flight would perhaps mean hotel bills, extra hire charges on the aircraft, etc. Sometimes it is business. But would the world (or even your job) really come to an end if you phoned up and said you couldn't get to that meeting? It might well come to an end permanently as far as you were concerned if you gave your presence at a business meeting priority over prudence as a pilot. Sometimes it is simply a matter of not losing face. You are a pilot aren't you, not a chicken? Real pilots don't give up when there is a little bit of low cloud or a forecast saying that thunderstorms or icing might be around, do they? But, yes, the fact is that real VFR pilots actually do just that thing. They realise that losing face is infinitely preferable to losing their life, which is quite often the only realistic option to abandoning the flight they had planned to make.

Personal Limitations

The limitations for VFR flight in various classes of airspace are legally laid down and every pilot should know them. But these need not necessarily be your own personal limitations. Only you know whether you are comfortable with the idea of finding a strange airfield in low visibility. The vis may be well within VFR legal limits but it could still be beyond your own personal ones. Are you competent to handle a crosswind at the destination aerodrome which is forecast to come close to the demonstrated crosswind limit of the aircraft? If not, then just don't set out to fly there until the wind shifts or abates somewhat. Honesty comes into the equation here. Just because other PPL pilots are doing things and seem to be getting away with them doesn't mean that you can or should or must, emulate them. The world of flying doesn't generally have policemen on hand to stop you from killing yourself. The one person who has the power to restrain you from doing something foolish is your own self as a sensible pilot. Don't let the pressures of family commitments, business appointments or financial economy override your own judgement as an airman.

Wherever you decide your personal limits lie in terms of visibility, acceptable crosswinds and cloud ceilings, there are two limitations which every private pilot who flies any light aircraft should invariably adhere to. The first is always to stay well clear of any bit of the sky where icing conditions are forecast and the second is never ever even begin to think that you and your little aircraft are any match for a thunderstorm. You may be able to cope with the torrential rain (although that can be heavy enough to drown a piston engine and associated hailstones can shatter windshields and damage airframes too) the lightning is likely to cause you or the aircraft serious damage, the thunder is totally innocuous but the air currents, turbulence, wind shear and down draughts found within and around a thundercloud, can contain the energy equivalent of a nuclear bomb or two. These forces are quite capable of tearing airliners to pieces, and I am not talking only of tropical thunderstorms either; a Fokker airliner was torn apart and downed by a thunderstorm over Rotterdam in the 1980s. Light aircraft stand virtually no chance of survival in the maelstrom that is the state of affairs of the vicious up and down draughts in the interior of every cumulonimbus cloud.

Good judgement is deciding to go by car or train or by scheduled airliner when the weather doesn't look like being within your limitations. Poor judgement is setting out anyway, just to 'have a look see', when you know full well that even making a start is in the end bound to commit you to trying to complete the flight. Good judgement is stopping somewhere to top up the fuel tanks when the weather at the destination looks doubtful. Bad judgement is deciding not to bother because a refuelling stop would take too long. Good judgement is waiting until the next TAFs are issued, rather than pressing on with the idea of picking up the latest weather from VOLMET en route. Good judgement is part of good airmanship and is probably the best form of life insurance that any pilot can have.

Your personal limitations can vary from day to day. Waken up tired after a long hard day and a short night's sleep and you may feel that you aren't really quite sharp enough to tackle conditions you would normally cope with quite happily. Again, be honest with yourself.

This business of making sensible weather related decisions about limits happens to be one area of life where two heads are quite definitely not better than one. Put two pilots of roughly equal experience and qualifications into one aeroplane and you will often find that neither wants to be the first one to throw in the towel. As a result both can find themselves in the air in conditions neither is happy about, each one fervently wishing that the other would make the obviously sensible decision. You should try very hard never to allow another pilot, or business superior, or even an air traffic controller, pressure you into flying beyond what you honestly know are your own personal limitations. On the other hand, sometimes two heads can be better than one if the 'second head' happens to be the partner of the pilot. She (or on the odd occasion he) is quite likely to be the one who makes the sensible decision, weather wise, and insists that the pilot abides by it.

Limitations also depend on other circumstances. Will it be necessary to come back later the same day, or is the return open-ended? Are you happy about the conditions whilst you are flying this particular aeroplane? How flexible are your schedules? Geography also has a bearing on the question. What might be perfectly acceptable weather for a trip to a well known destination may be very marginal for one you have never seen before. Low cloud cover over flat land in East Anglia or Denmark is a very different creature from low cloud cover in a mountainous country like Scotland or Switzerland. What may be acceptable in your home environment could be very much more difficult to cope with as a stranger in a foreign land.

When considering the question of weather limitations (as in many other aspects of flying) one of the best maxims I know is; always keep your options open. There is nothing worse than finding yourself totally committed to getting through to the only available landing place when the conditions there are marginal, to say the least. It isn't only IFR pilots who need alternates. You should always leave yourself with at least one alternative route and destination, in case conditions deteriorate or an emergency occurs. Try never leaving yourself without an 'out'.

First Find Your Forecast

Once upon a time (and to pilots who have recently arrived upon the scene this may very well sound just like a fairy story) every aerodrome of any size had a met forecaster on duty. If you were flying from one of those that did not, you could telephone (at normal phone prices) to the nearest aerodrome (civil or military) with a met section or to the local met office or weather centre, and have a chat with a forecaster there about the conditions you were likely to meet along the route you were planning to fly. If you phoned the day before they would actually prepare a comprehensive route forecast for you, METARs, TAFs, synoptic charts and all the rest clipped together in a folder waiting for you at the departure aerodrome. It was all part of the service, and even if the accuracy of some of the forecasts for more than the next hour or two was sometimes of doubtful accuracy, the service itself was a great deal better and safer than the service available to pilots today. If you did a reasonable amount of flying, you learned as time went on how some forecasters tended to be somewhat optimistic, seemingly wanting to tell you what they thought you, as a VFR pilot, wanted to hear. You soon learned to distrust those to some extent. You also came across the perpetual pessimists; if you followed their dire prognostications about fog possibly coming in early, the chance of thunderstorms building up; the probability that the warm front would stall and hang around for days, then you would hardly ever have got off the ground at all.

I well remember the days when Birmingham Airport had a manned met office with forecasters at the disposal of all pilots. One afternoon I was there receiving a long and involved briefing from a forecaster for my proposed VFR flight from Birmingham to Belgium. I cogitated over his advice, picked up the TAFs, METARs and synoptic charts, and thanked him for the information. As I was about to leave the office the Captain of a British European Airways Vanguard came across and quietly said, 'You know, old chap, you almost sounded as though you believed what that long winded bugger was telling you there'. Despite their failings, like most pilots who have experienced a personal forecast, I must admit I always have preferred that to anything that appears on a PC or Minitel screen, is heard on an automated phone system or spews out of a fax machine.

ALDERNEY   EGJA 031353Z 0315/0319 36007KT 9999 SCT022

BIGGIN HILL   EGKB 031412Z 0315/0322 30010KT 3000 BR FEW012 PROB30
                            1517 6000 TEMPO 0319/0322 1400 BR PROB40 1922 0600
                            FZFG VV////

BOSCOMBE DOWN   EGDM 031349Z 0315/0319 33008KT 9999 FEW012 BECMG
                            0316/0318 5000 BR TEMPO 0318/0319 3000 MIFG

BOURNEMOUTH/HURN   EGHH 031405Z 0315/0324 32009KT 9999 FEW010 PROB30
                            0317/0324 8000 BECMG 0321/0324 20010KT

BRISTOL   EGGD 031050Z 0312/0412 VRB05KT 9999 FEW015 BECMG
                            0321/0324 18014KT BECMG 0401/0403 7000 -RA BKN010
                            PROB40 TEMPO 0401/0406 18017G27KT 2000 +RA BKN004
                            BECMG 0406/0409 28017G27KT PROB30 0411/0412 7000
                            SHRA BKN009

BRIZE NORTON   EGVN 031324Z 0315/0415 33006KT 9999 FEW020 BECMG
                            0316/0319 4000 BR PROB40 0317/0323 0300 FZFG BKN000
                            PROB30 0323/0401 2000 SCT004 BECMG 0401/0404
                            17015G25KT 5000 RASN RA BKN010 TEMPO 0402/0408 3000
                            +RASN +RA SCT006 BKN008 BECMG 0407/0410 26013KT
                            9999 NSW FEW020 TEMPO 0410/0415 27015G25KT

CARDIFF   EGFF 031050Z 0312/0412 VRB05KT 9999 SCT020 BECMG
                            0321/0324 17010KT BECMG 0400/0402 7000 -RA BKN014
                            PROB40 TEMPO 0400/0407 18015G25KT 3000 +RA BKN007
                            BECMG 0405/0408 28015G25KT 9999 PROB30 0410/0412 7000
                            SHRA BKN014

CRANFIELD   EGTC 031412Z 0315/0320 30010KT 9999 FEW020 BECMG
                            0316/0319 24006KT 6000 PROB30 0319/0320 3000 BR

CULDROSE   EGDR 030748Z 0309/0318 03010KT 9999 SCT025 PROB30
                            TEMPO 0311/0315 -SHRA SCT020

TAFs for South England, South Wales and Channel Islands

Forecasting has, however, during the last twenty years of the 20th century, become much more precise, with sophisticated computer programs crunching data from all over the globe and producing fairly accurate forecasts that extend for several days ahead. These do go wrong occasionally but in general you can be reasonably sure that now at the start of the 21st century a TAF will not be very far off the mark. Just the same, it does pay any pilot to keep in mind a couple of little realised facts about TAFs and METARs. A METAR is a report; it was probably absolutely accurate when prepared, but it has become just history by the time you read it. A TAF is no more than a forecast; it is, at best, an educated guesstimate by some so called meteorological expert, which indicates what weather he or she believes is likely to occur in the coming hours. Mentioning expert forecasters takes me back to Colorado, where the US Weather Bureau once had to ask a Denver newspaper to stop publishing a very popular personal weekly weather forecast that appeared alongside their official one. The popular one, which more often than not turned out to be far more accurate than its professional counterpart, was produced by a 90 year-old who based his forecast on how the wound he got during World War I was feeling that particular week.

Weather Safety at a Price

Even if the METAR is brand new and the TAFs are all accurate ones, there is still trouble for the poor pilot. Unless you fly from a major aerodrome where they have all the data available (or, even better, the computer equipment to call up the very latest ones for you) the private pilot flying VFR has to get hold of this vital information independently. In Britain, during the 1980s politics forced the Met Office to start charging for aviation met, whether this was accessed by telephone, fax or, when it arrived on the scene, via the Internet. Premium rate phone numbers, deliberately slow speed fax polling and expensive connection charges all pushed up the price of this vital safety information and made it a seriously expensive business to obtain actuals, forecasts and charts covering a couple of hours flight from say the north of England to the Channel Islands.

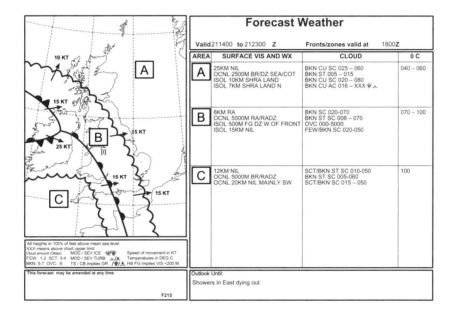

For some years the UK Met Office continued to levy charges to access Met forecasts on the internet, even though identical information could be downloaded from other French, German, Dutch and American web sites. Fortunately sense eventually prevailed and it is now possible for UK pilots with Internet access to download TAFs, METARs, basic weather charts and other information from the Met Office simply by registering free of charge on their web site. An annual subscription will allow you to access a fund of additional data including satellite images, thunderstorm information and other useful information too. But if you know your way around the Internet it really isn't all that difficult to get most of this additional information off other web pages, which are run without any subscription charges. It is important, however, to understand what is being downloaded here. Much of the data coming from these other websites originates from the UK Met Office but reaches UK web surfers via America perhaps, and may be a little out of date. The satellite photographs also can be confusing, if not downright misleading, to anyone who has doesn't have any experience of interpreting these. Private pilots are not expected to be qualified met forecasters, but the more background you can acquire in this direction, the better you will be placed to get the most out of sources of Met information like these.

A page of Metar actual aerodrome weather information downloaded free of charge from the UK Met Office website

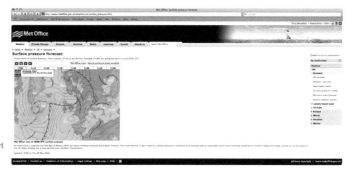

Looking ahead; this animated chart shows pilots the current weather situation plus the Met Office's idea of how things will look in 24 and 48 hours time. This service is also available free of charge from the Met Office website

The Air Navigation Order makes it mandatory for the commander of any aircraft registered in the United Kingdom to:

'… reasonably satisfy himself before the aircraft takes off that the flight can safely be made, taking into account the latest information available as to the weather reports and forecasts available and any alternative course of action that can be adopted in case the flight cannot be completed as planned.'

To comply with this a pilot is entitled to use up to date forecasts and reports obtained from sources other than the Met Office, such as the German or French weather fax services or other Internet sites. Some of these can be useful and inexpensive source of TAFs and METARs, satellite images and synoptic charts. Newspaper weather charts are next door to useless, being based on information that was obtained many hours earlier. On the other hand some televised weather forecasts can give pilots a reasonable idea of whether the weather is likely to be acceptable VMC or not. In the United States there is a dedicated satellite TV Weather Channel, with special aviation slots throughout the day, and you can find this Weather Channel running all day on TV sets at many FBOs and flying schools throughout the United States. It can be extremely useful to pilots but unfortunately, after it was given a trial period on European satellite TV in the early 1990s, that European weather channel was taken off the air again. All sensible pilots must brief themselves on the current weather situation by one means or another. That isn't just because it happens to be a legal requirement; it is because it is an eminently sensible safeguard against being caught out in conditions beyond your own personal limitations. But in the end, try always to remember that all METARs are no more than snapshots of what things were like at a given time in the past and TAFs are no more than one person's (or more and more these days, one computer's) idea of what the future might hold. Use them for guidance; don't ever be so naive as to assume they always contain the undisputed truth about the weather conditions you are going to encounter.

Marginal VFR

One of the most common situations in which PPL pilots flying VFR can get into serious trouble is when they find themselves without any reliable visual reference; without a horizon or sight of the surface you can quite easily and rapidly lose control of the aeroplane. This can happen to you while night flying, for instance if you unexpectedly fly into a cloud which can be virtually invisible to you in the darkness. It can also happen even in broad daylight and miles away from any cloud, if visibility drops too far. Other situations occur where pilots retain full control over their perfectly serviceable aircraft but end up flying into the ground, hills or other obstructions, for the simple reason that they don't see them in time to avoid them. Outside controlled airspace in the UK you, as a PPL qualified pilot without an IMC rating, may legally fly VFR in visibilities down to three kilometres; this means you can see no farther than objects which are just 48 seconds flying time ahead of you at 120 knots ground speed and a lot less if you happen to be flying something as slick as a Bonanza. Not a great deal of time to see and avoid, although for an alert and experienced pilot, probably adequate.

Fog has a nasty habit of rolling in, seemingly from nowhere, and turning good VMC into an absolute no go area for a pilot who is not instrument rated

The serious problems begin to rear their ugly heads when conditions deteriorate below the licence limitations. It is illegal to continue flight into such conditions but regardless of this, it can and does happen, for various reasons (including the reason that you may have had a forecast for good VMC all the way but it has turned out to be over optimistic). It is a fact that, even if the general visibility is at or just above a licence limit of 3,000 metres, there are going to be some places where it thickens up to well under that effective figure. A general overcast day with a cloud base of 1,200 feet may well seem fine for a local VFR trip, except that cloud bases are not always perfectly flat and can dip down uncomfortably low in places, perhaps in the very places where the topography of the land tilts up, just to make your marginal VFR even more marginal. Flying towards a frontal system can sometimes result in your finding yourself in deteriorating weather conditions that have already closed in behind you, and you could also be over terrain that gives little option for a precautionary landing. Foolishly pushing things to the limits like that can end up with you finding yourself well and truly stuck in marginal weather conditions. Just where you draw your own margin is very much up to yourself. For some pilots it is quite a long way above the official limits for licence minima. Other pilots may well be prepared to chance their arms right down to the official minima. No private pilot, however experienced, should take it one iota farther than that.

At one stage of aviation, before instrument flying became a serious possibility for pilots of light aircraft and before all the later big improvements in radio and navigation equipment during the 1950s, virtually all GA weather flying was done under VFR. Pressing on under a lowering cloud base and deteriorating visibility was known as 'scud running' and you had to have some prowess as a scud runner to have any kudos in certain flying circles. But back in these days there were very few 1,000 foot TV aerials, no mobile phone masts and much less regulated airspace to worry about. Aircraft tended to be slower too. Yet despite that, scud running occasionally scared these pilots out of their wits and not all that infrequently, it killed them. It still does. Accident reports continue to give as contributory causes to (frequently fatal) accidents such things as 'continued VFR flight into IMC' and 'controlled flight into terrain'. It is sad that there are still so many pilots who believe that licence limitations, flight rules and the rest of the regulations only apply to other people and not to themselves.

The best way of coping with marginal VFR is to adopt a few sensible tactics aimed at keeping you out of it. The object of a cross country flight is to get to the destination, but a good tactical pilot knows that it is even more important still to be alive to get there another day if conditions militate against it on the first attempt. Of paramount importance on a marginal day is a good flight plan. It is essential to plan the route in such a way that you will continuously have a close idea of where you are. A GPS moving map in the cockpit is fine, but don't blindly put your life in its hands. Plan your route to avoid natural obstructions like mountains, remembering that what is called orographic lifting can cause the cloud base to be considerably lower around mountains and high ground than elsewhere. Make it your aim to track alongside unmistakable line features as far as possible. Keep a finger on the paper chart all the way, replicating the job of the symbol on the moving map. Your chart is much more precise than your GPS for detail features like coastline shape. It shows all the roads and railways and has all the obstructions marked on it, which is more than you can say for all but the most sophisticated and expensive GPS moving maps. Just the same, having a GPS running as back up can be invaluable, especially if the marginal weather reaches your bottom line and you want to use its 'nearest airfields' feature to beat a quick and safe retreat.

Sooner is Better than Later

It is important never to delay that retreat too long. A shower of rain ahead can often engender the feeling that you will pass through it in a couple of minutes and things will be fine again on the other side. But a shower of rain in marginal conditions means the visibility is going to be significantly reduced, and probably means that the cloud base will be lower as well. Betting your life on an improvement on the other side is not good tactics. It is just tempting providence. As you fly into such conditions you may well be forced lower to stay clear of cloud; this brings you into the danger area for collision with hills or obstructions that you may only be able to see when it is too late to avoid them. The bad tactician, or the pilot whose flight plan has gone awry, is liable at this stage to panic, slam on power and pull the nose up trying to find a safe altitude. This is the stage where loss of control is quite likely to come into the equation. Even instrument rated pilots, who are in practice with their instrument flying, can find an unpremeditated transition from VFR into IMC like this very tricky to cope with. So what chances does the average private pilot have, with only rudimentary instrument training, or even the IMC rated pilot who is out of current instrument flying practice?

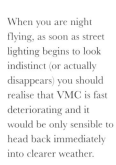

When you are night flying, as soon as street lighting begins to look indistinct (or actually disappears) you should realise that VMC is fast deteriorating and it would be only sensible to head back immediately into clearer weather.

When marginal weather conditions are prevailing, you will perhaps come across a pilot who pooh-poohs the whole thing and tries to persuade you that forecasts are always pessimistic. He knows the area well and tells you that just like him (it seldom is a her) you'll be able to make it okay. Peer pressure can sometimes be very difficult to resist, but if you believe your best tactic is to stay on terra firma then have the courage of your own convictions, not the bravado of his. And if you do take-off, only to find that your adviser was (as you probably expected anyway) totally mistaken, then don't continue flying into conditions you are unhappy about. Flying should be an enjoyable activity. It really is a shame to use it simply to scare yourself witless and probably put your passengers off flying for ever.

Advice About Ice

By the time many pilots have ceased to be students and have at last qualified for their PPLs, they have developed an almost morbid fear of ice. It is admittedly quite nice stuff to have in a gin and tonic, almost bearable in a carburettor since there is a pretty straightforward and well-known way of getting rid of it from there, but pilots find positively terrifying the thought of ice becoming involved with aeroplanes in any other way. The very words 'airframe icing' seem to have a chilling effect on them. This pathological fear of ice arises simply because all text books on aviation meteorology and airmanship carefully warn pilots over and over again of the dangers of airframe icing. Flying instructors then assiduously re-emphasise these solemn warnings in such a way that no student pilot can ever finish the PPL course and remain unaware of the ice hazard, which, like an evil spirit, is constantly lurking just around the corner. It is no small wonder that many pilots end up in such awe of icing that they refuse to take to the air at any time when the temperature is anywhere near, never mind below, freezing. As for planning a flight at or above the forecast freezing level, many pilots regard that as tantamount to attempted suicide.

A healthy respect for airframe icing is of course essential if you want to enjoy a long life and still like flying little aeroplanes. On the other hand the exaggerated level of dread of ice that many instructors, and a lot of flying training manuals, instil into student pilots' minds does tend to put an unnecessary limitation on their future flying activities. The fact is that, as a private pilot without an IMC or instrument rating, all you have to do to be certain of remaining clear of icing conditions is to stay strictly within the limitations of your licence regardless of the ambient air temperature.

Almost the only forms of airframe icing you are ever likely to encounter if you stick to this rule are the kinds that occur whilst the aircraft is on the ground. This can take the form of hoar frost, that forms when an aircraft has been parked in the open on a clear night at temperatures of zero or below or, very rarely, water that may have collected in the airframe (say at the bottom of a rudder or in an elevator where the drain hole is blocked) and then been frozen there. To ensure that your aircraft is airworthy it is of course essential to remove all of these forms of ice (together with any associated snow) before even thinking about taxiing out to take-off. Even thin layers of hoar frost on a lifting surface can seriously reduce the aerodynamic efficiency of an aircraft, sometimes to the extent that take-off becomes impossible.

These forms of ice apart, it is only on very rare occasions that a law-abiding VFR pilot might encounter another type of airframe icing. This is generally known as rain ice. This type of ice can form on an aircraft while it is in the air if the aircraft has been chilled by flying through significantly colder air and its temperature is still below freezing point when it happens to encounter a shower of rain. The raindrops are then liable to freeze immediately on contact with the cold aircraft. Alternatively, and again only very seldom in the UK, the same effect can also occur as freezing rain. On the very rare occasions that freezing rain is encountered, it is usually when raindrops from the clouds which are associated with a warm front fall through an inversion. These chilled raindrops will then immediately freeze into a glasslike layer on the first thing they contact, be that telephone wires, power lines, road surfaces or aeroplanes. Nasty stuff, presenting problems for almost all forms of transport. It is best avoided by pilots, either by staying on the ground when such conditions are forecast, or by turning through 180° and

This poor Grumman has been subjected to an extreme form of freezing rain airframe icing on the ground.

flying straight back out of the rain, as soon as it shows the first sign of forming ice on the airframe. Freezing rain, of course, actually makes up a bit for its nasty characteristics by frequently forming black ice on the roads and runways, which makes it very difficult for the pilot to drive to the airfield in the first place or to take-off even if he does reach there.

Flying is Fine in Frosty Weather

The fact that the air temperature may be well below freezing does not by itself mean that anyone flying VFR is foolishly asking for trouble from icing. Airframe icing will normally occur only when the aircraft is actually flying in cloud or in very poor visibility conditions (both probably outside the VFR limitations of your private pilot licence). Super cooled droplets in the mist or clouds can then build up into layers of clear ice, rime ice or hoar frost on the aircraft surfaces.

Very few aircraft of the types flown by private pilots are fitted with any form of ice protection, other than pitot head heaters, and virtually none of them are cleared for flight into known icing conditions. So even if you have followed the advice given later (see Chapter 6) and gone ahead to qualify for an IMC or Instrument Rating, you would still be going outside legal limitations (this time those of the aircraft rather than your own licence and ratings) were you to fly into icing conditions of the type described.

It is unfortunately true that not every pilot invariably flies 100% within the letter of the law, and some might decide to exercise the privileges of their instrument rating by climbing through a layer of cloud where icing was forecast, simply in order to reach clear air above it. Or, because icing conditions tend to be somewhat erratic and unpredictable, you might be flying happily along in cloud where the temperature is well above freezing, when suddenly you see with dismay the OAT probe, some rivet heads and then the corners of the windshield gradually beginning to vanish under a rough white substance. The first time this happens, because of all the frightening stories fed to you during your flying training, your immediate reaction will probably be one of horror. You just know that the aircraft is shortly going to look like one of the textbook photographs which appear to show aeroplanes being swallowed up by glaciers. But what probably happens next is that (while you are working out whether it is safe, terrain wise, to descend, or whether a 180° turn to rescue your aircraft from its imminent terminal dive will be accepted by ATC) you begin to realise that the machine is actually still flying, maintaining height and responding to the controls. It obviously has never read the textbooks about what it was supposed to do in icing conditions.

Once you then realise that you are not imminently in danger of dying and that an aircraft can in fact carry a certain amount of ice accretion without falling like a brick out of the sky, you are liable to say to yourself that icing is no big deal, and to begin believing that all these warnings you were given as a student were just plumb stupid. This is the perfect way to begin a dangerously complacent attitude towards icing. You experienced a light, short lived form of icing on this occasion, and were sensible enough to get the hell out of the area as soon as possible. Icing isn't always as bad as the warnings paint it to be but it certainly isn't guaranteed always to be as easy to cope with as you had it this time.

The first, second and final lesson about icing and airborne aeroplanes that you really ought to commit to memory is that time is of the essence. Every moment longer than necessary that you stay in icing conditions is one moment too long, a moment in which the windows become more opaque, the lifting surfaces lose more of their aerodynamic shape and efficiency, the weight of the aircraft increases. The sooner you get right out of there, the better for all concerned. Circumstances will dictate whether you should climb, descend or 'make a 180' and turn back; what you must never do is simply soldier on, hoping it will all go away like a bad dream.

If you ever should be unlucky enough to end up in charge of a really heavily iced aeroplane, you must be aware of the fact that it will almost certainly behave very differently from its normal self. With increased weight, disfigured aerofoil sections, opaque windshield and so on, you have to be ready for it to demonstrate decidedly unusual quirks as you try to bring it back in to land. With a modicum of luck, as you descend into warmer air most of the ice will melt away, but if there is freezing air all the way down to ground level you may not be so fortunate. Lowering the flaps on an iced up aeroplane can have highly unpredictable results and is generally highly inadvisable. This is so because the tail plane of a conventional aeroplane is designed to produce a down force to keep the machine stable in the air. But tail planes have sharper leading edges than wings and ice tends to form most eagerly on sharp edges (just look at the OAT probe, antennas, rivet heads etc). So the necessary down force from the tail is probably already severely compromised by ice that is completely invisible to you from your seat in the cockpit, and lowering flaps can seriously aggravate that situation, making the aircraft very liable to drop its nose sharply. Under these conditions it is better by far to pick an aerodrome with an adequately long runway and then come in to land flapless and at an appreciably higher than normal threshold speed, in consideration of the unknown altered aerodynamics and all the extra weight you may be carrying.

It is necessary for all pilots to keep a reasonable sense of perspective about airframe icing, in exactly the same way as it is necessary for them to keep issues like being unsure of their position on a cross country or contending with engine failure in sensible proportion. Be alert to the possible dangers, but don't allow them to colour your whole attitude towards flying and, as a result, spoil your enjoyment of it.

Choking on Icicles

Carburettor icing is something else entirely. It is not necessarily associated with wintry temperatures; in fact it is really quite likely to raise its ugly head when the ambient temperature of the air is quite warm. Due to the effect of evaporation of the fuel and the reduction in the pressure of the air as it passes through the carburettor venturi, the temperature of this air can drop very considerably. If the air being sucked in by the engine happens to contain a lot of water vapour this can freeze inside the system. The gradual reduction of airflow caused by the formation of this ice can cause an insidious drop in engine performance. This can come on so gradually that an unwary pilot might not even notice it at first, and might simply nudge the throttle open a little to compensate for the loss of power. Quite soon the power will drop off a bit yet again and if the pilot doesn't get the message, the aircraft will soon find itself with the throttle fully open and the power still inexorably easing off. A reduction in revs on a fixed pitch propeller aircraft, or an unexplained drop in manifold pressure in an aircraft with a constant speed propeller, are signs that should never be ignored in that way. Carburettor icing is very easy to contend with if caught at an early stage of formation, but if the pilot ignores the build up too long, and then it can be a very different matter. The engine can eventually lose so much power that it is no longer generating the heat necessary to warm up the hot air that is the only way the pilot has of thawing out the ice in the carburettor. A vicious circle, indeed.

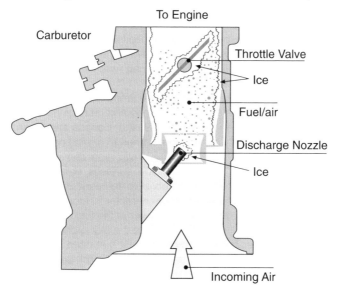

Every aircraft handbook has its section describing how best to handle carburettor icing and since these methods vary somewhat from one aircraft to another it is essential to know the system for each type that you are in the habit of flying. In general it is inadvisable ever to use partial carb heat as a preventive measure; this can actually encourage the formation of the ice that you are trying to avoid. Application of full hot air as soon as carburettor ice begins to form (or at other times as laid down for certain flight conditions or throttle settings) is what is normally called for. It is an action that can initially have some rather alarming consequences, as the engine begins to cough, snort, hesitate and run rough as it goes through the process of swallowing the water produced from the melting ice that has been the original cause of the power loss. Have faith however, and in a few moments the power will come back with a rush and you will soon be made aware of all those nudges you gave to the throttle lever before you realised what it was that was really going on. Keep the full hot air applied until you get out of the conditions that caused the ice in the first place. If need be, adjust the mixture to compensate for the lower density of the hot air. If you remain alert to the possibility of carb icing occurring and follow the aircraft handbook advice, this should guarantee that you never have any more than the occasional, very short lived, encounter with this other often over dramatized bogeyman of piston engines, carburettor ice.

Wonderful Weather for Flying

Most books about flying weather dwell (as I must admit I have done here to some extent too) on all the nastier aspects of meteorology that can make flying uncomfortable, dangerous or just plain impossible. There is, however, another side to this weather question. Pilots who allow themselves to become purely 'fair weather flyers' really do let a great deal of enjoyable flying pass them by, getting into the air only on days when the visibility is for ever, the sky is an unblemished blue and the wind is warm, light and steady. There are lots of other types of weather which can make practising your prowess as a pilot a thoroughly enjoyable experience. Don't let your prejudices prevent you from making good use of all the days when these conditions prevail.

What About Winter?

Take winter for a start. You really shouldn't stop flying just because the weather happens to have turned a little chilly. There was a time when only a few hardy souls, and the masochists among us, went flying in freezing temperatures when we had nothing but little open cockpit aeroplanes to fly, but almost all present day light aircraft are fitted with some creature comforts like windscreens, draught proofing and efficient heaters. The good old days of frostbitten fingers and icicles forming on handlebar moustaches belong to the past. Crisp, clear, frosty weather can make for superb visibility. Navigating by map-reading over a snow covered landscape offers a whole new experience to any pilot who has never encountered that enchanting scene before. Believe me, when you have done it once you certainly will want to repeat the exercise. It can be quite exhilarating and can reveal facets of the countryside below that you will never have seen in warmer weather.

Generally the British Isles are not affected by the extreme winter weather conditions that can turn engine oil into toffee, freeze greased controls solid and make engine pre heating essential before attempting to start. And even in regions like Alaska, Canada and Siberia, where extreme conditions like that do occur regularly, GA seldom comes to a grinding halt. Admittedly, even in the so called temperate regions never mind the arctic, you can end up with pretty numb fingertips after scraping hoar frost off the airframe surfaces before flying. Carrying out a thorough and careful pre flight inspection in sub zero temperatures also calls for a certain amount of stamina, perseverance and strength of character to stop you cutting the odd corner (such as kneeling down in the snow to inspect for water in the fuel system, perhaps?) but it can all certainly be well worth the effort involved. I find that the sky is often a wonderful place to be on a bitterly cold winter day, after the early morning mist that often follows a clear frosty night has burned off from the white landscape. Winter sunshine is weak and causes few thermals, so flying is much smoother than on a warm summer day. It's the ideal time to fly your air-sickness

Even if there is an inch or two of snow on the airfield, provided it isn't (as here) too deep to prevent a safe take-off, winter flying can be an eminently satisfying experience.

susceptible aunt, perhaps. Polar air tends to be free from industrial pollution and so visibility can be superb. Another winter plus point is that the sky is much emptier; less circuit traffic means more air time per hour. The RT frequencies are quieter and the whole sky is usually a lot more peaceful. Flying is much more relaxed than when you have to share the sky with everybody else on a busy summer afternoon. Winter scenery from the air can also be magnificent, especially in and around mountains; it is totally different from other times of the year. Night flying can be blissful too; clear hard frost with sparkling streetlights below and an ocean of stars above. All the pilots who lock up their logbooks and licences for the winter really don't know the sheer enjoyment they are missing.

Even the aeroplane seems to like winter flying. The higher density of cold air packs more energy into each engine cylinder than on a hot summer day, and so you actually have a marginally higher performance machine to fly. Its range is, in theory, slightly greater too, since cold fuel is also denser than warm fuel; as a result each tank carries a little more weight of fuel when full and it is the weight of fuel on board, rather than the volume, that determines the range of an aircraft.

Looking over my own early log books I see that I averaged more hours between November and February in the first few years of my flying career than I ever did between May and July. Much of that flying was done in Scotland and in open cockpit aircraft too. Yet, in retrospect at least, I remember it as in the main thoroughly enjoyable flying, of which I have many fond memories. Given due respect for the prevailing conditions, winter skies can often offer flying that is every bit as much fun as in any other season of the year. Many pilots actually prefer winter flying, despite its occasional drawbacks and difficulties.

Even Fog Can Be Beautiful

Fog is not a weather phenomenon that encourages many pilots to rush into the air. It can be downright dangerous to any non-instrument rated pilot of a light aircraft and yet, given the right conditions, it can occasionally provide pilots with an enchanting experience. When river fog is creeping slowly up a valley and spilling over the adjacent hills to blanket the countryside all around, the pilot's eye view gives a marvellous insight into the workings of mother nature and brings alive the pages of meteorology textbooks. Of course, if your home airfield happens to lie in the line of approach of this blanket of fog, you would be better not to prolong this practical weather study course to the point where a safe return to base becomes too touch and go. Occasionally too, after early morning fog has cleared from your base airfield sufficiently to

Radiation fog filling a valley like this can spread surprisingly quickly to cover an adjacent airfield.

permit VFR flying there may still be areas of it lingering in the vicinity, turning the usual workaday landscape into something almost ethereal. Lines of electricity pylons stride across an invisible landscape; the rippling light grey shroud covering the fields is broken only by occasional church towers, chimneys, rows of trees or areas of upland. Whether such flying is quite legal VFR is open to question; are you really 'in sight of the surface'? On the other hand, in the remote contingency of an engine failure under these conditions, you are surely in no more dangerous a situation than you would be were the same thing to occur during night flying or while flying over water. You can certainly enjoy this mystic scene of mist below you in safety, even in a single engine aeroplane, by keeping close to the boundary of the foggy area, while always remembering how quickly some types of fog can roll in.

The one way you should never plan to view a layer of shallow fog from above is when it is forecast to clear from your destination aerodrome before the time you expect to get there. It may look quite pretty thirty miles out but then begin to look nastier than pretty as you get closer and find to your dismay that it hasn't obeyed the forecast. The clearance of this type of fog is notoriously difficult for forecasters to predict and it is best never to rely on forecast clearance times. Under these circumstances, either wait where you are until you get a METAR from the destination confirming that it is clear of fog, or ensure you carry an adequate fuel reserve to allow for diversion to an aerodrome that you know is clear, and forecast to remain clear. Don't be caught out by local quirks of climate and topography either. Just because an aerodrome near to your destination is reporting clear of fog, it doesn't necessarily mean that the one you are heading for is also clear. Quite insignificant differences in height or nearness to water or hills for example, can make all the difference to the formation and clearance of advection fog, radiation fog and mist.

Not Getting the Wind Up

Wind tends to put many pilots off flying, especially if it is blowing at anything approaching right angles to the runway. You never know just when that is liable to be the very situation you find yourself in on arrival at an airfield one day, and so crosswind landings are something you should practice rather than treat like a plague and try always to avoid. The art of achieving a satisfactory crosswind landing is one that brings a considerable degree of smug satisfaction even to old hands at the game. If you had an instructor who tended to postpone the lesson every time the wind was being awkward, you owe it to yourself to find another instructor who is willing to help you master this gentle art. There are aficionados of the one wing low system and other pilots who swear by the crabbing approach. Some aeroplane types and some pilots seem to be more suited to one than the other but neither is wrong, so if you find the one your mentor is trying to teach you feels uncomfortable or is giving you a hard time, try the other one. Once you have mastered your chosen technique and feel you can handle a crosswind up to something approaching the aircraft handbook's maximum demonstrated crosswind figure, the sting should have vanished from crosswinds. A small refinement you might like to add to crosswind techniques, under appropriate circumstances, is to break with the habits of a lifetime and ignore the white line down the centre of the runway. If the crosswind is strong, your take-off or landing roll will be short, and if the runway involved is a reasonably broad one the simple expedient of starting the take-off, or touching down, in one corner, heading as much into the crosswind as possible, can pay dividends. If you have a 25 knot wind that is 40° off the runway heading then you are contending with about 16 knots of crosswind component; slew at least the initial part of your landing or take-off roll by even 10° into wind and the crosswind you have to wrestle with has dropped to just 12 knots. It can make an appreciable difference, but does need a bit of practice too. And that is another reason for not being shy about flying on windy days. Use them to get yourself into practice for when you'll need it.

When the windsock shows a stiff wind like this at right angles to the runway, it is probably a good time to decide whether or not the wind is within the aircraft's limits and within the pilot's capabilities.

Brighten Up your Day

The sky is leaden; a layer of stratus hangs over the airfield and seems to stretch to infinity. Not much of a day for flying, is it? And yet, even on a dull looking day like this, the weather has several flying plus points. The air is pretty stable and free from thermal turbulence, so provided the cloud base is acceptably high and precipitation isn't affecting visibility too much, it can be not a bad day for a bit of circuit practice, or for taking someone with a susceptible stomach up for a smooth little flight. Also, since this type of cloud usually indicates settled weather, if you don't make use of it, you are quite possibly going to have to wait rather a long time for anything better to come along.

Don't Let Rain Stop Play

The TV weather map is covered with these black clouds with rain symbols below them and half suns peeping out above them. If it's going to be rainy then there's no point in flying, is there? If you were to adopt that as a firm philosophy then, certainly so long as you are based in the United Kingdom (or in much of the rest of Europe for that matter) you would find your flying activities being very severely restricted. Refusing to fly any time there is a chance of the aircraft going through the airborne equivalent of a free car wash, does very considerably cut down on a pilot's flying activity. As mentioned elsewhere, the torrential rain associated with cumulonimbus thunderstorm clouds is something you must avoid at all costs, but the steady drizzle from reasonably high nimbostratus, or the short sharp showers from ordinary cumulus clouds are relatively innocuous to aircraft. You can usually avoid isolated showers of rain in order to maintain better visibility, but areas of light rain are not normally the cause of drastic reductions in visibility. Admittedly, heavy drizzle does tend to go along with high humidity and visibility down to under 3,000 metres. Rainwater also blows off the windshield of a light aircraft without any appreciable restriction to the pilot's vision. (That is one reason why the manufacturers don't bother to fit them with windscreen wipers.) If the rain happens to be associated with an approaching frontal system with steadily lowering cloud base, deteriorating visibility and worsening weather, then any thoughts of flying should be reconsidered and VFR flying would probably be inadvisable. So far as isolated showers are concerned, those typical of the cold sector after a front has passed through are only one of the features of what is actually an air mass that can make for really pleasant flying conditions.

Snow showers are somewhat different. For a start, even moderate snow has a drastic effect on visibility from an aircraft, and you are unlikely to be able to maintain VMC whilst flying in anything more than very light snow. Dry snow normally flutters harmlessly past aircraft without causing any airframe icing, but flight in sleet or wet snow can result in air filters and engine air intakes becoming blocked by ice accretions. Since virtually no light aircraft are cleared for flight in known icing conditions, simply obeying these aircraft limitations should keep you clear of this hazard.

Inclement Weather Can Make Flying Fun

It always seems a pity when people who you feel should really be enterprising pilots turn into dyed in the wool fair weather flyers. By spurning the challenges and fulfilment of flying competently through a bit of precipitation and around a few clouds and by always avoiding sub zero temperatures or stiff crosswinds they deny themselves a great deal of what flying has to offer. The obvious end result of that is that these pilots will never really able to make full use of their licences. Except in extremely favourable weather situations (more often to be found in places like South Africa or California than in Western Europe) they will always be reluctant to undertake anything more than local flights, and will miss out on much of the potential that a pilot's licence should bring with it. Don't allow an irrational mind-set like that to restrict your flying. Accepting the occasional weather challenge and seeing the sky in many of its moods, benign or otherwise, is all part and parcel of being a pilot.

It is only by experiencing different sorts of weather that a pilot can come to understand it. Pretty pictures and neat diagrams in textbooks are all very well, but only by flying through something a bit more interesting than clear blue summer skies will you come to understand the element in which you are going to spend the flying hours of your life. Feel the wind under your wings on a blustery day. Learn to enjoy the sensation of flying through rain showers the way you used to enjoy splashing through puddles as a kid. Find out what it is like to fly on a frosty winter night with black overcast above you and a fairyland of colourful city lights below. Provided you accept your own limitations and those of the aircraft you are using, and provided you fly consistently within these limits, this type of flying should never expose you to any unacceptable risk. It will, on the other hand, enable you to do so much more with your licence, add so much to your experience of airmanship, enable you to pilot the aircraft on visits to more

It can be fun to flirt with these medullary (or crepuscular) rays that look like searchlights shining down from the heavens, seemingly trying to target little aeroplanes as they fly through them

places and generally add to your overall enjoyment of being a pilot. If you opt out of this challenge and stick in the rather less exciting rut of a purely 'fair weather flyer', you will never experience the wonderment of seeing the silhouette of your aircraft in the centre of a multicoloured, perfectly circular rainbow against the clouds, or enjoy the magic of watching a full moon rise above a broken layer of stratus, or experience the joy of chasing medullary rays shining down like celestial searchlights from above.

Chapter 4
Different Environments

No Angst about Airports

If you are a newly fledged pilot and have done virtually all of your training at a small airfield or even at a relatively quiet regional airport, then the idea of flying in for the first time to a busy international airport can look like being quite an adventure. Even a cursory study of the UK VFR Flight Guide published by AFE or a look through Pooleys Flight Guide will soon confirm your suspicions that coping with the traffic and controllers at a major airport are likely to be a whole new ball game compared with what you have considered as normal circuit procedure up till now. And it certainly is. But, like many other aspects of flying, all that you really need in order to get rid of the apprehension you feel is a clear understanding of what is actually involved. Remember, if you had been trained at a flying club or school based at perhaps Manchester, Glasgow or Birmingham International airport, you would probably be just as worried about your first attempt to carry out an overhead join at a grass aerodrome possibly without any radio, or at best only a ground/air radio instead of full ATC service.

The very diversity of the aerodromes that are available for you to use is one of the major advantages of flying as a GA pilot. To rule out any category of these from your plans for future flying would be to cut off your nose to spite your face, as the old saying goes. Within my own first fifty hours of flying I had visited only a meagre eight airfields, each of which was fairly small; the busiest of these was Fairoaks. (at least Fairoaks is still active; of the others I flew from in those days, Portsmouth, Hamble and Ouston have all closed and the futures of a couple of the others seem to be hanging in the balance.) My log books now show take-offs and landings at well over 500 airports, airfields, landing grounds and strips, many of which conjure up special memories and meanings for me. It is quite marvellous how so many aerodromes have managed to retain a special character of their own, despite the stereotyping that has occurred at most of the major ones.

The recent requirements for increased levels of security have led to the disappearance or sanitization of such things as airport visitors' galleries. Even non flyers used to participate in some of the excitement of aviation at these places with their cameras and binoculars bringing an air of enjoyable family activity on the 'ground side' of the airport that no groups of seriously minded 'reggie spotters' ever can. Unfortunately many of the smaller airfields now also have their share of fencing, security barriers, no entry signs and policed or locked doorways leading to airside. All of this is sadly a sign of the times in which we live, but it certainly does detract from the enthusiastic and exciting atmosphere that many of our aerodromes used to have. Fortunately there are still some around that have managed to preserve something of their earlier character, despite what has been foisted upon them by contemporary circumstances.

Airfields Worth Exploring

There are still many GA airfields around that are genuinely interesting places to visit. In Britain, for instance, we are lucky still to have airfields like Barton. This was once Manchester's main airport and decades of aviation history mingle here with present day enthusiasm for light aviation. Flying clubs, home builders, young and old, airmen and women all congregate at Barton. The access by air may be cramped under Manchester TMA, the runways are not over long by current standards and the grass does get a bit muddy in wet weather, but I always find the atmosphere thoroughly enjoyable. Yorkshire has a near equivalent to Lancashire's Barton too; Sherburn in Elmet. Sherburn has added a hard surface runway to its selection of grass runways which means that it is always possible to find one that is more or less into wind (but don't be tempted to use what looks like a vast concrete runway alongside the aerodrome; it isn't a runway any more). Again, here you will meet a real grass roots enthusiasm, a touch of WW2 nostalgia in places and, just like Barton, you can generally be sure of a good honest bite to eat. Glenforsa in Mull is another marvellous airfield. A level grass runway lying between the

There are few facilities at Eddsfield, this private grass airfield near Driffield in East Yorkshire, but there is an excellent welcome for visiting pilots, B & Bs not far away and some beautiful surrounding country to explore by air or on the ground.

purple mountains and the sparkling sea with a fully functioning hotel/restaurant within a few paces of the field. Walking, angling, mountaineering and sight seeing are all available practically on the spot. Another island airfield I enjoy whenever I visit it is Texel in the Netherlands; call the Tower 20 minutes out and they'll have your overnight B & B arranged and a hire car or bicycle waiting for you by the time you have parked the aircraft. At the other end of the scale I have many fond memories of some very large and busy airports too. Among this category within the UK I give Birmingham, Newcastle, Bournemouth and Norwich high praise for the efficiency of their handling and the general facilities they make available for pilots of small aircraft. Unfortunately, the same cannot be said about the costs involved in a flying visit to some of these larger aerodromes, especially those operated by British Airports Authority. Once you add up all the relevant landing, parking, handling and navigation charges it can set you back quite a bit. They could perhaps take a leaf out of the books of much bigger and busier places elsewhere in the world. Some years ago I was astounded by the comparatively low charges made by Frankfurt and Amsterdam Schiphol, for the excellent service they gave me in slotting my relatively slow four seat piston single, into their hectic traffic stream of jet airliners and then making room for it to park on the GA Apron. Their costs have risen somewhat since then, but at least they still make room for GA visitors, which is more than can be said for some airports not a million miles from the UK capital, where light aircraft are either not accepted at all or may reluctantly be offered a slot but at absolutely prohibitive charges. If you are considering trying to get yourself some practice in big airport procedures I would certainly not advise you to pick Heathrow, Gatwick, Edinburgh or Stansted for that exercise. Nor Munich's new airport where similar regimes exist, despite the fact that other busy commercial German airports like Berlin Schonefeld, Nuremberg, Stuttgart and Dusseldorf still remain reasonably user friendly towards light aircraft.

Easy to spot from the air and replete with facilities (radio, nav aids, ground services etc.) major airports, such as Edinburgh seen here, tend to be expensive to use and are not always particularly user friendly towards light aircraft.

I have flown small Cessnas, Pipers and Grummans in and out of many big airports in the United States, places such as Atlanta, Nashville, San Jose and Memphis, and I have seen there how light aircraft can be incorporated into the traffic pattern with no more than a reasonable bit of savvy and co-operation between Air Traffic Control and the pilots involved. In most of the United States and in many other countries it appears to be an accepted part of aviation that international airliners, commuter flights, business and private aircraft can, and do, share the same airports, airspace and facilities.

Private Pilots Play Their Part

For smooth integration of commercial aviation and GA to take place at major airports all the pilots involved must be on top of their jobs, none more so than the light aircraft jockeys whose mounts are appreciably slower than the majority of users. Busy controllers have little time to spare for 'say again' requests from private pilots who have been unable to anticipate what the next call was likely to be. Nor do they welcome long winded pilots whose RT transmissions take up too much airtime. Quick, alert, clear and concise transmissions are what is wanted here. It may all sound pretty bewildering on first acquaintance (which is one good reason for having an instructor or a more experienced fellow pilot along on your first trip into such an airport) but it soon falls into place and becomes almost second nature. It really does; even to the pilot who was brought up in the more casual surroundings of 'Little Grassfield on the Hump'.

Some pilots from places like Little Grassfield are in considerable awe of 'real' airports with Approach, Tower and maybe Radar and Ground control, Automated Terminal Information Service (ATIS) and the rest. They feel scared of making a botch of things and having their performance reported to the CAA. But ATC is not there to write tickets.

Their aim is simply to keep their traffic flowing safely and efficiently; your aim should be to co-operate in helping them achieve this. If your inexperience does occasion a minor slip, ATC are almost invariably prepared to turn a blind eye, provided you are honest with them. To avoid making such minor errors, the best thing to do is to emulate the Boy Scouts, and 'be prepared'. As mentioned in Chapter 2, if you have the chance to do so, listening to airport RT procedures on a hand held or scanner receiver can be a big help in preparing yourself. It gets you familiar with the sequence of instructions, the phraseology used and the conciseness expected of you, long before you actually fly into the area. In many cases ATC actually makes flying a lot easier for you than it is when you are operating from a smaller airfield. Your first task, if the airport has an ATIS frequency is to listen to it and make a note of the information it gives you. Then when you call the initial contact frequency, tell them you have 'Information Kilo' or whatever its code letter was at the time. In America, even when there is no ATIS broadcast, some pilots say every airfield still does have its ATIS; by listening out on Tower frequency you can glean in advance from ATC conversations with other aircraft which runway is in use, what the wind is, QNH, QFE and any significant weather factors. In the States, saying you 'have the numbers' as part of your initial 'who you are, where you are and what you want to do' contact, sometimes allows the controller to save time and breath; this is not correct in the UK.

When inbound towards a major aerodrome, it helps a great deal if you make full use of your transponder.

It you wish to enter controlled airspace you must have a working transponder on your aircraft. ATC will allocate you a squawk code enabling them to identify you on their radar screens. Radar or Approach will feed you instructions to manoeuvre you into a suitable position relative to the runway and to other traffic, and then Tower is likely to slot you into a gap in the landing sequence without you having to make any effort on your own. You will, as often as not, be allowed to approach the airport direct from your present position, either on a straight in approach or onto right or left base. It does make life a lot easier for you than the procedure to which you are better accustomed; being locked into standard overhead joins and full circuits at uncontrolled airfields. All that is required of you at the bigger airport is to acknowledge the instructions and do precisely what you have been told to do. The more conversant you become with ATC procedures, the easier it all becomes. Occasionally it is only after you roll towards a stop on the runway that you find your troubles really beginning.

At places like this you don't simply backtrack to the one and only exit from the runway. You will more probably be told to do something like 'vacate at the third exit on your left and contact Ground on 121.350' after which Ground are quite likely to come up with a series of instructions about 'Link Charlie, taxiways Golf, Juliet and Mike, North Apron and Stand 38' or other things of that nature. If the VFR Flight Guide you are using does have an airport diagram page with all that guff on it, do be sure to have it open and ready for action. If it doesn't, then do try, before you set out, to photocopy or borrow the appropriate page from someone who has more comprehensive IFR or AIP Guide. Assuming you have Internet access, it is also possible to make use of the AIS's wonderful web site and to download bang up to date aerodrome data from there, including airport approach charts and layout diagrams. Without an airport diagram in the cockpit you can really find yourself up the creek without the proverbial paddle, annoying Ground Control who will then have to give you a long series of 'Next left' and 'Second on the right now' instructions to help you find your parking place. Which doesn't make you exactly the flavour of the month with the controllers and that attitude can unfortunately tend to rub off onto other light aircraft visitors arriving at that airport following your visit? If in doubt stop and ask.

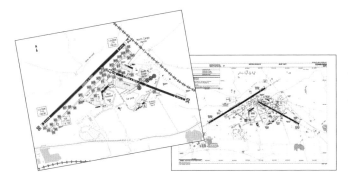

Without an aerodrome chart like this CAA one or an equivalent (UK VFR Flight Guide chart far left) you can cause awkward problems both for yourself and for the controllers when you fly in to visit a major aerodrome.

Conversion Course for Uncontrolled Airfields

The other side of the coin is the pilot who is familiar with flying at an ATC controlled aerodrome and yet pretty green about how to get in to one of these odd places where voices that seem to be masquerading as controllers say odd things like 'Land at your discretion' instead of giving you a normal clearance. Exercising your discretion is, after all, more difficult than simply obeying instructions, isn't it? As I said above, major airports can in some ways be easier for you to fly in to than small airfields. Where full ATC service is not provided you may encounter either Flight Information Service (call sign 'Information') or aerodrome Air/Ground Communication Service (call sign 'Radio') or you may find yourself at an airfield or airstrip with no RT service whatsoever. The idea of unregulated persons operating the ground end of the radio, or the very thought of landing at a place where there is nobody at all to talk to, fills some big airport trained pilots with considerable apprehension. Before you let that feeling build up too strongly, it is as well to remember that it really isn't all that long ago that very few light aircraft carried any radio at all, and that many of these small airfields and airstrips all around the country safely handle thousands of aircraft movements every year with minimal or no RT contact at all.

Wherever you trained, you will have learned the basic aerodrome circuit (or 'pattern', for those readers who did their training in the States). It is this simple circuit that forms the basis of flying in to these smaller airfields and strips. If you managed to achieve your PPL without making a non-radio approach and landing then I would suggest your instructor was a little remiss; you should get that omission rectified. Ask an instructor for a verbal explanation of a standard overhead join, dead side descent and circuit procedure and once you've got that into your skull, have the explanation followed by a practical demonstration with your instructor alongside you. It may initially seem odd compared with what you are accustomed to. You do certainly have to make the occasional decision yourself which ATC may up till now have been making for you, but there is no great mystery or magic involved. Where there is nobody watching from the tower or following your blip on a radar screen, it is up to you even more than usual to keep your eyes peeled for other traffic and to maintain your own separation from it. Working out all by yourself without ATC to tell you, from just a careful study of the signal square and windsocks, which runway is in use, what direction the circuit is being flown, what the wind direction is and strongly it is blowing, is perhaps a new experience for you, but aviation lived that way quite happily for years before radio came along to make us all a bit lazier and less observant. Where the airfield has a radio frequency, even if this is unmanned, it is often a useful practice to listen for and to make calls known as 'traffic advisories', but these do not necessarily paint a complete traffic picture; there may be other aircraft around flying non-radio. It is a similar situation when you use the UK's Safetycom frequency at airfields which have no allocated VHF frequency of their own. When you are within 10nm of a non-radio aerodrome and below 2,000 feet aal you are encouraged use the 135.475 MHz Safetycom frequency to let other traffic know your whereabouts and intentions to help avoid potential collisions. (It is not, however, intended as a general 'chat' frequency.) You must again remember that not everyone in the vicinity will necessarily be using Safetycom and don't forget that we still have a few non-radio aeroplanes flying, as well as non-radio aerodromes. Once you have got the hang of this type of smaller aerodrome operation in UK there may be a surprise waiting for you when you venture abroad. Circuit procedures, joining especially, can be very different in other European countries, despite JAR harmonisation and all that. A flying visit to the United States will bring you into contact with the joys and jumbled radio calls of their Unicom system. And you can read some more about that subject later in this Chapter.

Going to Grass

With the constant increases in the cost of operating aircraft from licenced aerodromes, landing, parking and hangar charges, there has been a significant increase in the use of small grass strips in the UK. We still have a long way to go before we reach the situation in the USA where there are somewhere around 15,000 active aerodromes, of which approximately 10,000 can be classified as grass strips or fields. Or to express that more correctly, they are what is termed 'unpaved'. Most of these are grass surfaced, but others can be of gravel, cinders, sand or just trodden earth. In the UK most (with the exception of Barra's runways which are of beach sand) at least purport to be grass, although some come pretty close to being just plain dirt at certain times of the year and mud at other times. Before heading off to make your first flight in to one of these little airfields, you would be well advised to have someone more experienced than yourself in strip flying come with you and show you the rudiments of the game. Most of these fields are fairly short, so a thorough revision of your short field techniques would not come amiss, especially if you have reached that big airport frame of mind where you now regard anything less than 2,000 metres as a short field. It is also essential to learn all you can about your proposed destination, from AFE's UK Flight Guide, Pooleys Flight Guide or from Lockyear's Farm Strip and Private Airfield Guide. This last publication concentrates very much on these smaller airfields and provides excellent contact details to let you obtain the essential prior permission you require before setting out for visit them. Virtually all of these places are private property and it is only polite (as well as being a requirement) to phone the owners in advance to notify them of your desire to pay the place a visit. This is also an excellent time to find out the up to date situation and the condition of the field or strip. Are there livestock grazing on it? Is the field soft or waterlogged? Is it in fact open? Has anybody perhaps put up a mobile phone transmitter mast on the approach or slung some telephone wires between poles just off the threshold since your guide was printed? These things happen and it is much better to know about them before you get there. That is one very important reason for complying with the Prior Permission Requirement (PPR).

Not all grass airfields are quite as easy to spot from the air as Sutton Bank, thanks to the famous White Horse right alongside the runway.

A grass surface requires you to adopt a rather different landing and take-off style compared with hard-surface runways, especially if the surface is rough or undulating. Tail wheel aircraft in general fare better than tricycle undercarriage aircraft on grass but, provided you reduce the loads on the nose-gear, even the latter can be flown perfectly safely and successfully from grass. I have based a typical tricycle gear 'spam can' four seater at a grass strip for many years and I know of at least one American owner who regularly operates his Learjet from grass. Grass strips are often a lot closer to where you want to fly than the nearest licenced aerodrome and if you are prepared to treat them with a little respect and use good judgement, there is no reason why you shouldn't include some suitable grass strips in your list of destinations.

Sadly, they have an unfortunate tendency to camouflage themselves into the background, looking like just one green field among so many others, so accurate navigation is often needed to find them. This is one aspect of navigation where GPS can be an invaluable help to you. Enter the coordinates for your airstrip destination before you start the flight and with GPS guidance you'll have little or no problem in picking out the correct field quickly. Once you have found your landing strip, set up a well judged approach and wait for that exhilarating feeling of dropping gently down onto nature's greensward with scarcely a sound from the tyres. That's ever so much nicer than the usual squeal of expensive rubber being rasped off by asphalt and concrete runways.

It can often be quite tricky to identify a grass airfield when it is surrounded by dozens of similar looking fields in varying shades of greens and browns.

Most grass airfields in the UK only have single runways although a few, such as Ashcroft in Cheshire, Shotteswell, near Banbury and Little Gransden near St Neots, do offer a choice of grass runways. Runway lengths vary, but only occasionally are they long enough to allow pilots of conventional tricycle undercarriage aircraft to fly in without doing some careful sums first. The maths involved is simply checking from the aircraft Owner's Manual or Pilot's Operating Handbook (POH) the exact landing and take-off distances required by the aircraft at the weight involved, and correlating this with the actual air temperature and wind velocity. The handbook figure must then be factored appropriately using the data provided by the CAA in their AIC on take-off, landing and climb performance of light aeroplanes (currently AIC 127/2006 (Pink 110)), though this gets regularly updated). Grass surfaces can require greatly extended take-off and landing distances as compared with concrete or asphalt surfaces. The difference can be as much as 35% if the grass is wet and less than eight inches high, and up to 60% for landings on short, wet, slippery grass, to give just a couple of examples. Some farm strips have been laid out on ground that slopes appreciably, sometimes from one side to the other as well as uphill and downhill. This significantly affects performance figures and you must also take this into consideration. The basic rule here is very simple. If you are at all doubtful about your ability to get in to any particular strip and out again in safety, just forget it. There are lots more places to land and no strip owner welcomes bent aeroplanes cluttering up his little airfield.

They (and more particularly their neighbours) don't welcome noisy visitors either, so for their sake (and for the future existence of the strip too, in case it is under threat from local protesters) please fly especially quietly and considerately in its vicinity. Keep to the approved circuit procedure, avoid flying directly over noise-sensitive places (which you should enquire about if they don't automatically tell you when you telephone them for that prior permission) and avoid dragging your aircraft in on a noisy, long drawn out low approach under high power.

And once you have rolled to a stop don't forget to turn first to the left after landing and have a good look round for other traffic, even if you know you are the only aircraft for miles around and the parking area happens to be to the right. There just might be someone else flying in, about whom you were blissfully unaware. Then move clear of the landing areas as soon as possible just in case someone else does want to use it.

Making use of little fields like these gives a whole new feel to your flying. Dropping in (after getting that essential prior permission) to a peaceful grass strip to meet like minded friends, to have a picnic perhaps, or to overnight in a convenient pub or a nearby hotel or B & B, is a totally different experience to flying in to even a small licenced aerodrome. The informality appeals greatly to many pilots; even if the more hide bound big fielders amongst us may find it unappealing. Care must be taken though, to ensure that not too much of the informality creeps into the actual flying. Grass strips demand a higher degree of precision flying than bigger airfields. They can, and not infrequently do, punish pilots who have the temerity to treat them with too casual an attitude.

There can be very few better ways of using a light aeroplane than flying in with the family to visit a pleasant little grass airfield and enjoying a picnic in the sunshine there before flying home again, perhaps by another route to see some different scenery.

Other Countries; Other Customs

As has been said several times already, there is a lot of fun to be had from flying in foreign lands. British based pilots must first overcome any innate reluctance they may have about flying over water in order to experience the joys of flying in the rest of Europe if they want to do that flying in their own or a rented G registered aeroplane. If you are one of these pilots who is not convinced of the fact that aircraft engines have no means of telling whether they are over land or water and run just as reliably on air with a traditional whiff of seaside ozone in it as they do anywhere else, then you probably should pick as short a sea crossing as you can. From England to the nearest landfall in mainland Europe is a mere 19nm and, with no controlled airspace under FL65 between Dover and Calais, you can fly VFR, weather permitting, at say 4,500 or 5,500 feet. From 5,500 feet in a typical four-seat single, of average performance, you have a still air gliding range of around nine nautical miles with the propeller wind milling. Thus, on the short passage across the Strait of Dover, there is only a very brief interval of time when you couldn't suffer a total power loss and still be able to glide to land on one side or the other without even getting your feet wet. Similarly, only 22nm of salt water separates southern Scotland from Northern Ireland and so even those pilots who remain slightly nervous about over water flight should be able to reach Ireland without too much anxiety.

Pilots of light singles frequently tackle quite lengthy stretches of water, quietly confident that their aero engine will keep on turning in exactly the same way it has always done over land. Flying from Scotland via the Strait of Dover for a visit to Scandinavia is rather a long way round and the 270nm Aberdeen to Stavanger route is used by quite a few VFR pilots every year. It means a fraction over two hours out of sight of land in an average light aircraft, but with appropriate survival equipment on board this seems to worry some pilots very little. Compared with the way singles are regularly ferried across the Atlantic via Greenland and Iceland it is indeed a mere nothing in terms of water crossings.

Renting Abroad

Not all private pilots have enough of the true Charles Lindbergh spirit in them though, and luckily there is an alternative way of flying abroad which might have a much greater appeal for them. This involves simply taking ferries or scheduled airlines to the chosen area and then renting a suitable aircraft once you get there. Within Europe at the time of writing there are very few complications concerning validation of JAA PPLs to allow you to use these when flying as pilot in command of locally registered aircraft in many countries. This situation is steadily improving, and very shortly all that will be required to pilot a light aircraft in any of the JAA countries will be a European licence issued under the JAR/FCL regulations. That, together with the normal check out with an instructor that will almost certainly be asked for by whoever is renting the aeroplane to you. Outside Europe the situation varies. In the United States the FAA will issue an Airman's Certificate quickly and easily on the evidence of your own national licence see www.faa.gov for further details. Elsewhere regulations vary from what is little more than a cursory glance at your logbook and licence, to what amounts to almost going through another PPL written examination and GFT. It can often be well worth the effort though. I have lasting and wonderful memories of the flying I was able to do following a morning spent studying New Zealand's VFR regulations and then passing an examination about them in a stuffy office in Auckland. It opened the door to a pilot's paradise of lakes and islands, miles of sandy beaches, volcanoes, hot springs, glaciers, fjords and some of the friendliest flying clubs and most fascinating flyers in the world. And having all the local rules and regulations fresh in my mind also helped me to relax and enjoy all these wonderful holiday flying experiences.

VFR Variations

When in foreign lands, it is important not just to assume that what you have come to regard as standard practice while flying in your home country will also be accepted as the normal way to behave there. So far as regulations are concerned, perhaps the most important point to remember is that a UK pilot flying a UK registered aeroplane is subject to both UK law and the law of the state in whose airspace he or she is flying. Once you have studied the VFR regulations for some foreign states you may well find that it appears a pilot may do certain things in another country's airspace that you are not allowed to do in the UK airspace. However, for safety's sake it is probably best always to assume you are restricted by both sets of rules and regulations and to fly accordingly. Most states in Europe keep fairly closely to the ICAO Standards and Recommended Practices (often referred to as SARPS) and where local rules do differ the differences are always listed in that country's AIP

Even the definition of what is VFR varies from country to country. In some countries, currently including France, Belgium, Norway, the Republic of Ireland, Italy and Germany 'VFR on top' (i.e. flying above a closed layer of cloud, out of sight of the surface) is permitted (provided you can get up there and back down again without going IMC). In many other countries it is illegal. Some pilots seem to believe that an 'imaginary hole' in the cloud layer below them somewhere near their destination is sufficient to enable them to comply with 'VFR on Top' regulations in those countries where this is permitted. Possibly it may be, provided their navigation is perfect (or their GPS doesn't lead them astray) but they should never forget the words of the famous French author and pilot Antoine de St Exupery "If a pilot is wrong just below the sea of clouds begins eternity".

The limitations that define exactly what Special VFR means actually vary considerably from one European country to another and sometimes (as in France) they vary even between one aerodrome control zone and another within the same country.

Many countries either totally forbid VFR flying between sunset and sunrise or it is so severely restricted it as to make VFR night flying virtually impossible. In other countries it is perfectly legal. In the UK all night VFR within a CTR has to be Special VFR, whilst outside controlled airspace all PPL holders who have a night qualification may fly at night, provided they observe normal VFR weather minima, quadrantal cruising levels and minimum height rules. Such flights are actually being conducted under IFR so far as the law is concerned, but they can be executed by pilots who do not hold Instrument Ratings (or even IMC Ratings) virtually as if they were VFR flights.

VFR above a closed layer of cloud is quite legal for pilots without any form of instrument flying qualification in many European countries (though not in the UK) but you must be able to get up there and back down again in VMC.

The IMC rating does not exist outside the UK and holders of an IMC rating are prohibited from using any of its privileges outside UK airspace.

Also the UK's quadrantal height rule is used only in a few countries of the former British Empire which have for some reason decided to retain it. In its place, before flying in most other countries of the world, you should familiarise yourself with the semicircular rule that is used almost universally elsewhere. This specifies that, above 3,000ft for tracks from 000°M to 179°M you should fly at FL35. FL55, FL75, FL95 etc up to FL195 while for tracks from 180°M to 359°M you should fly at FL45, FL65, FL85 etc up to FL185.

Skulking along, keeping safely and legally below the base of the airways system is part and parcel of normal VFR flying in UK airspace. However, in much of the rest of the world you'll find that either airways virtually don't exist below FL100 (as in Germany and the USA) or that VFR traffic is permitted to fly within the airways system, at least up to a specified flight level (as in the Republic of Ireland, France, Belgium, Spain, Portugal, Denmark, Greece, Switzerland etc). In the Netherlands, VFR traffic is banned from operating within any airways, in a similar fashion to the rules that apply within UK airspace.

The system used when you are approaching aerodromes with control towers, follows much the same routine the world over, but there are some European countries (e.g. Switzerland) where the use of Visual Reference Points (VRPs) is not just optional, it is mandatory. This makes it essential for you to have with you all the appropriate landing charts either taken from a flight guide or from the relevant AIP. Fortunately nowadays most aerodrome information like this is available free of charge from the various national aviation authorities' web sites for download. Even if these landing charts and aerodrome diagrams are not legal necessities in other countries I would certainly recommend you to have them with you wherever you go. It certainly does make life simpler, both for you and for the controllers, if you know the general layout of the place in advance and are ready to recognise the names of the VRPs, whether prosaically called 'Echo' and 'Sierra' etc. or more exotically known as, for example 'L'Isle sur la Sorgue' or 'Chateau Salins'.

When you are heading for a small GA airfield in a country other than the one you normally fly in and you are expecting to have to make a conventional circuit join, don't assume that these conventions here will necessarily be the same as they are at home. They very probably won't

Safer probably, and certainly more prudent, until you are proficient in instrument flying, to restrict your VFR flying above cloud layers only to well-broken layers, where you can always see a safe route back down again.

be. Circuit heights can vary from as little as 500ft above aerodrome level to 1,200ft or more. In Germany the joining procedure is similar to the one generally used in UK, but in France locals expect you to descend over the aerodrome to join downwind from the inside of the circuit at about the mid point of the downwind leg. In the United States you are expected to join downwind from an angle of about 45° again about midway along it, but this time from the outside of the circuit. (And you should try to remember that the word 'circuit' is pretty meaningless in the USA; call it the 'pattern' and they'll understand you better.) In the Netherlands a standard join is similar to the American one, except that you are expected to approach the downwind leg at 90° to it, not 45°, and then to turn right or left depending on the circuit direction. Belgian pilots are generally taught to join the downwind leg right at its start, by coming in towards it from a long way upwind. This system does have the advantage of letting pilots size up the circuit traffic situation pretty thoroughly before they actually join it. As a visitor in a foreign land you are expected to conform to local circuit procedures, so you strongly advised to do a little serious investigation of this subject from Flight Guides or from the national AIP (which is probably available to you on the Internet) in advance.

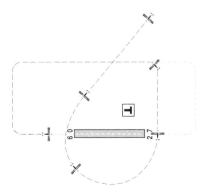

UK trained pilots are used to joining the circuit as shown here, but this procedure is by no means standard in other countries.

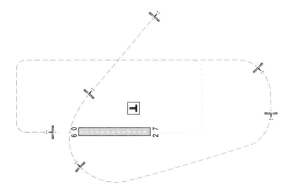

This is the normal procedure used for joining the circuit in Belgium.

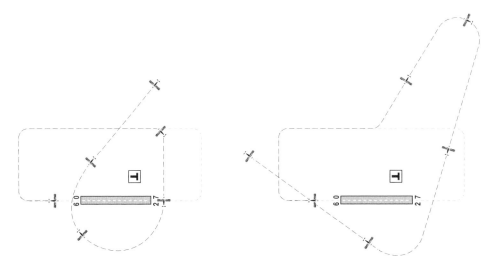

There are at least two recommended ways of joining circuits in France.

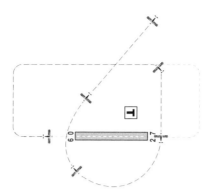

This is the normal procedure used for joining the circuit in Germany.

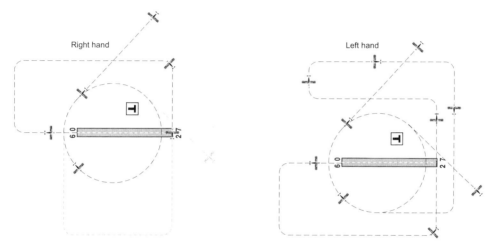

In the Republic of Ireland they join circuits differently from the UK procedure. This shows the accepted methods used there for left hand and right hand circuits.

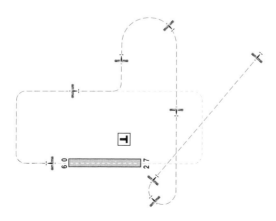

This is the normal procedure used for joining the circuit in the Netherlands.

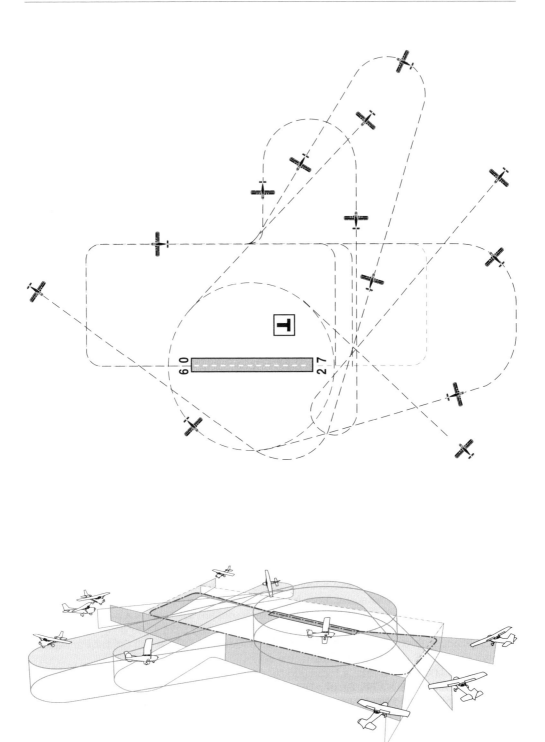

If a group of pilots used a selection of the various circuit-joining procedures taught in various countries around Europe it could result in an extraordinary state of confusion at the aerodrome concerned.

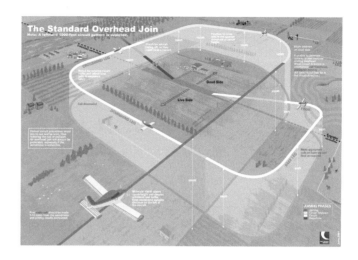

Minimum height rules are another area where unsuspecting visiting pilots might find themselves under misconceptions. The UK's current 'no closer than 500 feet to any person, vessel, vehicle or structure' is liable to be revised soon, but at the time this book is published still leaves low flying down to just a few feet agl across open moor land legal, provided you avoid any animals, hikers or houses by at least 500ft horizontally, diagonally or vertically. But be warned, that rule certainly does not necessarily apply everywhere else. The French have a complex table of minimum heights relating to what you are overflying and what type of aircraft you are flying. For single piston engine aircraft, 1,000 feet is required from factories, hospitals and motorways, 1,500ft from small gatherings, towns and herds of cattle and so on up to 4,500ft for large built up areas and gatherings of over 100,000 persons. The AIPs of certain countries actually specify that it is forbidden to fly underneath bridges or similar constructions but even when this veto has not actually been put into printed words, you are still probably wise to assume it does exist!

The process of adapting to local conventions while flying abroad is greatly eased by getting hold of a copy of the local AIP and spending a good few hours studying it before venturing into the air. Fortunately nowadays many states make available on their AIS websites what they believe to be the most important extracts concerning VFR flight from their respective AIPs. To find these, the Eurocontrol website www.eurocontrol.int/ais/ is a good starting point because it has links to most European AIS websites. Or, to take a few examples, information about France can be obtained directly from www.sia.aviation-civile, gouv.fr; for Belgium use www.belgocontrol.be; for Germany try the Deutsche Flugsicherung website at www.dfs-ais.de/ and for Spain use www.aena.es/.

For France, the Guide Delage also makes a good starting point if you understand enough French (although Pooleys do now have an edition of Delage available with English translations) and the French AIS publish an indispensable set of four 1:1,000,000 VFR charts, a 1:250,000 chart of the Paris area and a VFR Guide. This set is updated every April and November, so make sure you have the current set before you set out to fly

The Guide Delage is an excellent VFR guide to use for flying in France and for Germany the little Flieger Taschenkalender is a useful reference to have, although both do require a certain basic knowledge of the native language.

in France. Many other countries (e.g. Germany, Belgium, and the Netherlands) publish special official VFR Guides to assist VFR pilots visiting their lands. Jeppesen Airfield Manuals contain some useful basic information about local procedures but most countries still seem to manage to keep the occasional surprise to spring on their visiting pilots.

There are for example, things like Germany's flashing yellow lights at the end of the runway. These are not simply visual navigation aids, they are illuminated to prohibit take-off or landing of powered aircraft during glider operations. In France the frequency 123.50MHz is the AeroClub 'common', much used for local chat (and many French pilots are so dreadfully disappointed to find it doesn't apply outside their own skies that they still persist in using it regardless!) Over Greece it is illegal to take photographs using telephoto lenses. In Norway there are large wild reindeer areas where flight below 1,000ft is forbidden. The Norwegian authorities sell a useful money-saving season ticket that can pay for all the landing charges that a foreign registered aircraft less than 2 tonnes incurs for seven consecutive days. The Spanish take PPR especially seriously. If an aerodrome is listed as PPR in the official Aerodrome Directory then you absolutely must have prior permission before you may even enter it into a flight plan as an alternate, never mind actually land there as your destination. In Sweden there are three so called 'N areas' and it is forbidden to fly in any of these unless a flight plan has been submitted either 20 minutes before take-off within the area, or 20 minutes prior to flying into it. If you manage to do any VFR flying in the United States you will undoubtedly soon encounter their infamous 'Unicom' system of VHF RT communication. This is an aeronautical advisory service in which many airfields all share the same VHF frequency, so you are liable to hear a cacophony of pilots' voices all calling traffic advisories for different aerodromes in the vicinity. Since Unicom should only be used while you are close to the airfield in question and since all calls should be prefaced with the name of the aerodrome you are using, what looks like a recipe for RT chaos actually works out reasonably well, as is proved by the fact that Unicom has been used successfully for many years all over the United States. As mentioned in Chapter 2, a generally similar system known as Safetycom has now been introduced for use in the UK at aerodromes which have no designated VHF frequency allocated to them.

Unusual UK

If you have done most of your flying in UK airspace you may well be beginning to think by now that it would be so much better if other countries could arrange their VFR as simply and sensibly as we do here. Think again. Pilots visiting our skies have to become accustomed to UK peculiarities, which don't appear on any ICAO charts; two different sets of SVFR minima, one for PPL holders and one for PPL holders with a mysterious thing called an IMC Rating that exists nowhere else; Regional QNHs, a concept unknown anywhere else; a total ban on flying in all that virtually empty airspace that forms the lower levels of UK airways; LARS, which they will never have met under that title anywhere else; and that famous and almost unique quadrantal rule already referred to above that takes the place of the semi-circular rule that the rest of the world knows and uses.

One day perhaps the JAA, or its successor EASA, will manage to harmonize VFR throughout Europe. The FAA doesn't tolerate differences like these between California and Florida, or Texas and Idaho. This undoubtedly does make flying under VFR around the USA a great deal simpler than flying VFR around Europe. However, variety is said to be the spice of life and there is no doubt that these varied European interpretations of the basic ICAO Visual Flight Rules do keep pilots alert. They also help to add quite a lot to the variety and enjoyment of flying around this continent under VFR as a private pilot. It is, for British pilots, an approximate aeronautical equivalent to the driving on the 'wrong' side of the road that makes continental motoring seem so distinctly 'foreign' to most British motorists.

Chapter 5
Flying and Finance

Covering the Costs of Your Flying

Throughout your time as a student pilot, the cash flow was all in one direction out of your own pocket and into the coffers of the flying club or school that was providing your training. Now that you have your new PPL tucked safely in your probably somewhat empty pocket, your mind may well soon turn to thoughts about just what, if anything, you can legally do to ease the financial burden that is involved in making use of your licence.

If the establishment where you trained is one of those where they require all their fleet of aircraft most of the time for flying training work, they may well have decided to set a fairly expensive price for you to hire these machines for solo flying or touring. Because of this, you obviously want to look around for a somewhat less expensive place from which to rent your aircraft. The hourly rates for solo flying do vary surprisingly, even for similar aircraft with similar levels of avionics and other equipment. A check through the 'Where to Fly' supplement that appeared in 2008 with Pilot magazine for instance, showed that the hourly rate for solo flight in a Cessna 152 can be as little as £101 in one place and as much as £150 in another. Four-seat aircraft rates likewise are far from standard throughout the country; C172, Piper Archer or Grumman Cheetah aircraft can be hired for about £115 per hour from some clubs, whilst elsewhere pilots can be asked for well over £170 per hour for similar machines. OK, the level of avionics and other equipment in the different aircraft will certainly vary a bit from one to another and other factors, such as whether an expensive club membership is involved and whether local landing charges are, or are not, included in the quoted hourly rate, also significantly affect these flying rates. You should be sure to find out about and consider these items when you are weighing up the various rates on offer. None the less, even a simple comparison like this shows that a little shopping around the local area can often be quite a help in reducing the negative flow of your hard-earned cash each time you rent an aircraft to fly.

One of the few ways in which a PPL holder can legally carry out what is known as "aerial work" is to fly, unremunerated, as pilot of a aircraft used for sky-diving or parachuting at a club of which he or she is a member.

There is, of course, one very big question to answer in connection with your future flying. Should you really go on renting aircraft to fly at all? It might very well be a much better plan for you, depending on all the relevant circumstances, either to buy a share in an aircraft or to become the outright owner of an aeroplane yourself. These options are dealt with in more detail in Chapter 8. There are many other ways of cutting the costs of your flying, although I have to admit that not all of these involve flying 'conventional' light aircraft. These cost-saving measures can include moving to microlights, piloting home-built aeroplanes, taking up paragliding or sky diving, becoming a sailplane enthusiast or jumping off mountains as a hang-glider pilot. We take a look at the first of these (microlighting) also in Chapter 8, together with the idea of building your own aircraft. Parachuting and gliding in all their various forms are, however, beyond the scope of this book, which is intended essentially to show private pilots how much enjoyment they can derive from making full use of their licences, and conventional Private Pilot Licences do not really have all that much bearing on these other airborne activities.

PPL – No Licence to Print Money

Enjoyment you can certainly get from using a Private Pilot's Licence; income you definitely must not. A Private Pilot's Licence entitles the holder under the Air Navigation Order to fly as pilot in command, or co-pilot, of any aeroplane within the aircraft rating included in the licence, subject to the very important exclusion of 'flying any such aeroplane for the purposes of public transport aerial work', or 'not for remuneration'. As a Private Pilot you are allowed to carry out aerial work only in a very few strictly limited ways. If you have a flying instructor's rating you are entitled to give flying instruction and to carry out flying tests provided you, the student and the aircraft, are all part and parcel of the same flying club and is not remunerated. Similarly, a UK CAA PPL who is the member of a gliding or a parachuting club, can undertake aerial work so long as this is limited to towing a glider or flying an aircraft used for dropping parachutists, again provided the aircraft is owned or operated by, and all the people concerned are members of the club involved. Even then though, no PPL holder is entitled to receive any remuneration for flying the aircraft. The sole exception to that rule is when the aeroplane is a microlight or a self launching motor glider and it is being used for instruction or testing on that type of aircraft, and provided that you have an appropriate instructor's rating. In that case you may receive remuneration for the instruction given or the testing conducted. Otherwise, as a private pilot you are prohibited from receiving any remuneration what so ever for any of the flying you do or payment in kind.

Another legal requirement makes the matter of financing your PPL flying even more problematic. This is the requirement that any operator of a UK registered aircraft who utilises the aircraft for public transport must hold an Air Operator's Certificate (AOC) issued by the CAA. This applies even if the aircraft is to be used in this way for only one single flight. The definition of a 'public transport flight' is very simple and straightforward. It is 'any flight which carries passengers and/or cargo for valuable consideration'. And that 'valuable consideration' can be taken to mean simply, if the owner or operator gains financially or otherwise from the fact that the flight took place. The CAA has prosecuted a number of uncertificated operators who have transgressed this all embracing law. Both the pilots and the operators also run the other risk that their insurance company might well wriggle out of its liability in respect of any policy if an aircraft was found to have been used for public transport without an AOC being held.

It is also legal for a PPL holder who is a member of a gliding club to act as pilot of an aircraft used to tow gliders at that club so long as the pilot is not receiving any payment for doing the flying.

Sharing Expenses

It is, however, legal for the holder of a Private Pilot's Licence to share the expenses of certain types of flight without the operator being required to hold an AOC. The pilot must always bear a proportional share of the actual costs of the flight. This means half the total costs if there are two on board, one third if three people fly together and one quarter if there are four in the aircraft. No more than four persons, including any children, may be on board. The flight must not have been advertised, except that when it is a club aircraft it may be advertised within the club and all on board must be members of that club and over eighteen years of age. The pilot must not be under contract to, or employed by, the operator of the aircraft. Abide by these rules and, although you obviously cannot make a profit, you can (at least so long as you can find suitable co-pilots or passengers to accompany you) reduce the effective cost of your flying.

As a PPL holder you are permitted to share the expenses of a flight with your passengers, provided you as pilot bear a proportional share of the actual costs of the flight; for example 25% of these costs if there are four people in the aircraft.

If your employer is prepared to reimburse you the actual costs of a flight made for business purposes then, provided you were not actually obliged by your employer to make that flight, you can, as a private pilot, legally reclaim these costs. You break the rules if you try to make a profit from the flight, but you can recover all the actual costs involved. This is relatively easy to do if you are renting or hiring the aircraft being used. You can reclaim the actual hire cost as invoiced to you, plus any landing charges, parking or hangar fees incurred, and fuel and oil bills. But the situation is less clear cut for the owner pilot. Claiming back from your employer a sum equivalent to the cost of alternative transport might be perfectly OK from your boss's point of view, but might not satisfy the CAA. A business class air fare or the price of a first class rail ticket might be considered to represent more than the actual costs incurred in using the aircraft, thus giving you as the pilot a financial benefit on the deal. Even if you were to use the equivalent cost of travel for the same journey in your own car (using the so called Fixed Profit Car Scheme (FPCS) mileage cost figures as approved by the taxman) this might still cause

CAA eyebrows to be raised, even though your tax inspector would almost certainly accept the figures. To claim back the equivalent of what the hire would have been for a similar aircraft from a nearby club should be acceptable, but even then lawyers could argue that this must include a certain element of profit. The only legally watertight procedure for the owner pilot would be to reclaim purely and simply the direct costs of the flight (fuel, oil, landings, hangarage etc) and to swallow hard and ignore such things as depreciation, insurance, maintenance etc since it can always be argued that these would still have to be borne, whether or not that specific business flight had been undertaken.

Exceptions to the Rule

If you are into competition flying, you as a private pilot can, within limits, actually earn something from air racing. You are permitted whilst flying with a PPL to collect prize money (or remuneration in the form of fuel/expenses) up to a value of £500 per event. Whether this would ever cover your actual costs of practice, entry and competing in the event is another matter entirely. And after all, you did it for the honour and glory, the fun, thrills and excitement and not for the money anyway, didn't you?

If you fancy air racing, like this event at Reno Nevada, then if you happen to win, the CAA allows you to keep up to £500 of your winnings for each event.

Provided you obtain permission from the CAA for a flight in aid of a registered charity (in advance of the flight) you are also allowed to collect payment for the flight, on condition that this payment (and that means all of it without any deduction for expenses or anything else) is applied for the benefit of the charity. Again, I have to admit that this doesn't do anything at all for you in the way of helping you to finance your flying, but at least it is one way of getting some hours into your log book that should make you feel good too, at least for a while.

There is only one other set of circumstances in which money can legally be paid to a PPL in connection with the cost of flying, and that is detailed in Chapter 8 where the question of group ownership of an aircraft is being considered.

In addition to the few legally permitted forms of remuneration described above, you will probably hear about lots of other wheezes by the use of which some club bores and hangar pilots claim they have managed to cover the costs of at least some of their flying. Some are downright contraventions of the law. You hear about such exploits as the chap who flew a couple of blokes who were in a tearing hurry to get to the Isle of Man and who 'covered the cost of the petrol' with a wad of well thumbed twenty pound notes. This is blatantly illegal, brazenly immoral, probably uninsured and is certainly depriving air taxi operators and qualified commercial pilots of their bread and butter. In the same way, no private pilot is permitted to accept any form of remuneration for the transportation of goods. That applies equally whether these 'goods' are nothing more than an urgent letter, or someone's ashes to be scattered from the air, or a whole cabin full of freight. To do so is to act illegally, to risk prosecution and the loss of your licence. That sort of behaviour is simply not acceptable.

Grey Areas

Some indirect forms of remuneration do however appear to be borderline cases, despite their not appearing to be authorised by the Air Navigation Order. Take for example the private pilot who flies off by light aircraft to some romantic place on holiday and writes up his or her exploits for Light Aviation, Pilot, Flyer or possibly (if it was that sort of holiday) for National Geographic or perhaps Cosmopolitan or GQ Magazine. If our hypothetical pilot with literary leanings is lucky (or is a particularly good writer) the cheque he or she receives in payment for the article might possibly more than cover the cost of the holiday flying involved. Could that be construed as receiving remuneration for the flying? Or would it always be accepted that the flying was only incidental and that any such income was payment purely and simply for the writing? If a PPL holder undertakes flights with the specific objective of photographing stately (or not so stately) homes, hotels or factories etc and then proceeds to sell these photographs to defray the cost of the flying, this amounts to undertaking aerial work illegally. That is quite definitely excluded from the privileges of the PPL.

Taking aerial photographs of peoples' residences or industrial premises with a view to selling them to the owners may seem like an innocent pursuit for a PPL holder, but this is classed as "aerial work" and it is therefore illegal.

But on the other hand, the circumstances could be that in the course of a normal pleasure flight a private pilot took some aerial photographs, and then later decided to enter some of these for a newspaper competition and one of these happened to win a nice cash prize. Or possibly some of these photographs might later be sold, maybe quite a long time after the flight on which they were taken, as illustrations for a book. In such cases it appears to me (and here I must emphasise that I am not qualified as a lawyer) that it would be difficult to prove that any income of this nature had arisen from the pilot having carried out aerial work illegally, without a commercial licence and the necessary AOC.

If in Doubt, Ask an Expert

One must remember, however, the old adage about the law being an ass and this can at times tend to leave the poor private pilot wondering where exactly the line should be drawn between inadvertent infringement of the law and innocent enjoyment of the hobby of flying. If you end up confronted by any situation of this nature, best get hold of an authoritative book dealing with aviation law and study it carefully. Then remember that if you are still in any doubt about some aspect of whatever is afoot, you ought always to err on the safe side. Tax experts often give their clients the advice that bending the tax rules and statutes is one thing but breaking them is quite another. In the case of PPL holders and aerial work the situation is similar; be careful that you do not cross the line, blurred and indistinct as that line sometimes may appear to be.

There are many other instances, as I am sure the reader can imagine where some form of income could arise either directly or indirectly from private piloting. If you are ever invited or tempted to tackle anything of a doubtful nature my advice to you is to avoid it like the plague. If it is something that looks to you as though it really might require an AOC, don't touch it, even with the proverbial barge pole. If anyone tries to inveigle you into doing any form of paid flying that falls more properly within the province of a CPL or ATPL qualified pilot, it is much wiser not to take the risk. If you yield to the temptation to do anything of that nature you are much more likely to put your licence into serious jeopardy than you are to help defray some of the costs of your flying.

Tax Breaks

There are certain ways in which some pilots can reduce the effective cost of their flying by making use of tax concessions and relief on Income Tax, Corporation Tax and VAT. There isn't much scope here for you if you are taxed conventionally through the PAYE system, but if you are fortunate enough to be running a business of your own you could possibly benefit. In order to do so, it is necessary to justify any claim for tax relief associated with an aeroplane in terms of the relevant Income Tax and Corporation Tax Acts and their current interpretation. You have to take care here too. The said interpretations (and the Acts themselves) are constantly changing as Chancellors, courts and appeal bodies go about their work. This is a positive minefield for the unwary and I strongly suggest that any reader thinking about trying to claim tax relief in connection with flying light aeroplanes goes straight off to consult a professional tax adviser. I am not an expert in that field (any more than I am a lawyer) and these paragraphs are not in any way intended as a guide to gaining tax relief for a private aeroplane. Unless you can convince yourself that your aircraft has really been, or will be, of use to your business, don't bother trying to convince the tax authorities. Only legitimate claims have any real chance of success.

There are two different sets of people involved here. One of these bodies is the Inland Revenue, who deal with Income and Corporation Tax and the other is Customs and Excise, who administer Value Added Tax. Their approach to the question of the use of an aircraft within a business may not necessarily be the same. To claim back the VAT on the purchase of an aircraft it is necessary to justify to the VAT Office that the aircraft is a business asset, similar, tax wise, to an office desk, word processor, delivery truck or warehouse. This usually requires proof that it is actually used either as business transport or for advertising purposes. If you claim it is being used for business transport, be careful; you could then fall foul of the requirement that you must have a Commercial Pilot's Licence before you can legally do aerial work. If you claim it is used for advertising, the advertising logos on the aircraft must be prominent enough to be seen and your business should be of such a type that this form of advertising might reasonably be expected to attract new customers to it. If the Tax Inspector can be convinced that the aircraft really is playing an important role in your business, then you may be able to claim capital allowances, which have the effect of spreading the cost of the aircraft as tax relief over a number of years. There are certain further advantages in having the aircraft accepted as being part of the business. Many of the operating costs, such as fuel, maintenance, hangarage and insurance can become business expenses and (assuming your business is VAT registered) the VAT can also be reclaimed on many of these items. Finally, if your personal tax position should ever come under close scrutiny, it could be very useful to have all your aircraft costs already neatly accounted for in the business books, rather than have a cynical Tax Inspector querying how you can possibly afford to run an expensive plaything like an aircraft on the meagre taxable income that you are declaring!

Borrowing Money for Training

The matter of borrowing money to finance the purchase of an aircraft is dealt with later in this chapter, but there is at least one other type of loan that could interest some private pilots. This is an advance to help pay for flying training towards advanced ratings and qualifications. If you're ultimate intention is to make a career as a commercial pilot there are several UK banks which currently operate loan schemes which they make available to embryo CPL pilots for this purpose. These systems and regulations do tend to change fairly frequently and for that reason (plus the fact that this book is not really designed for the private pilot who is heading for a CPL) these are not listed in detail here.

The Real Risk of Up Front Payments

If you are wealthy enough to pay in advance the whole (or a substantial amount) of the fee for any particular flying training course, it is often possible to obtain what sounds like quite an interesting discount on the basic price. If you are dealing with a well established school or club this is quite frequently a very sensible way for you to cut down on the cost of the advanced training. However, pilots should always be on their guard here. In rather too many cases where this discount is heavily promoted by the establishment concerned, it has proved to be a symptom of the fact that the school was in a distinctly unsatisfactory financial state. It probably was, in fact, in dire need of the advance payment in its coffers to keep itself financially afloat. If, as sometimes happened, the flying establishment went bankrupt before the pilot's course had been completed, he or she was left high and dry with no qualification, no cash, and often precious little chance of recouping much of the advance deposit as an ordinary creditor of the bankrupt establishment. There have even been a few cases of deliberately fraudulent operations being set up simply to collect as much as possible in the way of cash advances from unsuspecting pilots, before the perpetrators vanished into the night, complete with all the gullible pilots' cash. Check the credentials of any establishment carefully before you decide to part with any flying training fees up front like this.

Looking for a Loan

If on the other hand you are less affluent, you may need to obtain a loan towards the not insignificant costs of training for an IMC rating, multi engine rating or PPL/IR (see Chapter 6). There are several potential sources of cash available for these purposes, although I am not aware of any schemes designed specifically for private pilots (as opposed to commercial pilots) who want to train for advanced qualifications. Many high street banks seem reluctant to lend money for anything that is in any way connected with private flying, but some bank managers do seem to be more relaxed about this and are quite prepared to consider a loan for advanced flying training. This normally only happens for pilots whom they already know as existing customers of the bank and who are considered by them to be suitable borrowers. Banks will usually make the proviso that the loan is secured on a life insurance policy or on your home always assuming that your home is not already mortgaged up to the hilt.

If your own bank manager cannot or will not come up with what you require, there are other sources of outside finance worth looking at. If you keep your wits about you and juggle the balance over at the right time from one credit card to another, zero interest balance transfer schemes can be a very inexpensive way of getting your hands on a few thousand pounds for at least a temporary period. Many financial institutions are prepared to grant secured loans, normally using property or life insurance policies as the necessary security, but pilots applying for one of these loans as new customers can expect to pay quite a bit over the odds in interest. Likewise, loans can be had, based on your own personal credit rating, from other finance companies and credit brokers. Several of these have departments specialising in aviation loans and will generally be quite happy to advance cash to be used for flying qualifications, aircraft purchase, engine replacement etc to pilots whom they consider creditworthy clients. The classified advertisements at the back of Pilot and Flyer magazines are good places to look for the phone numbers and addresses of such companies. Also pilot members of AOPA UK will find that this organisation has links with one or two finance companies who would be prepared to consider making money available to them for these purposes. Be sure you are aware of all aspects of what you are taking on before you sign on any dotted lines though. As the advertisements say, your home may be at risk if you fail to keep up the repayments on any mortgage or other loan that is secured on it. Also, many loans of this nature are significantly more expensive in interest terms than a straight overdraft would be if you could persuade your bank to give you the cash for your advanced flying qualification in that form instead.

To the outsider, private flying has always carried with it an aura of enormous expense. It is generally considered to be a sport or pastime available only to the very affluent. However, to most enthusiasts, private flying is an activity for which sacrifices have to be willingly made. If your flying activities get to become too much of a strain (either on the finances or on the spare time) for you to be able to keep other activities like golf or skiing going, then if you are a keen pilot these just get demoted in your order of priorities. For the real flying enthusiast, if the family car is still running well, then it is always better to carry on running it for another year or two, rather than buy a new model that would eat into your flying budget. If a half hour in the club's nice shiny 180hp four seat tourer swallows up too much of your monthly pay cheque, then a couple of circuits in the clapped out old two seat trainer is certainly better then no flying at all. If you find enough fun and fascination in your flying, you should almost always manage to find enough finance to keep flying somehow.

Loans to Buy Aircraft

In Chapter 8 we take a look at the pros and cons of aircraft ownership and (just in case you find that there are more pros than cons in your own case) this chapter would not be complete without some consideration of how to go about financing the purchase of an aeroplane of your own.

By far the most economical way always is to buy the aircraft out of capital if that is an available option in your own circumstances. The loss of interest on a savings account is invariably a great deal less than the interest you will have to pay on any form of loan you take out for this purpose. Unfortunately not all PPL holders with an urge to become aircraft owners are in the fortunate position of having the necessary amount of cash available or easily realisable.

It pays to be careful and compare what is on offer from various banks and other sources when you are trying to arrange finance to buy an aircraft.

As mentioned above in connection with bank loans for flying training, not all bank managers have a very high opinion of light aviation. Although they are usually quite happy to lend money for their customers to purchase Peugeots or Porches, they take a very different attitude towards a customer whose mind runs in the direction of Bonanzas or Beagles. A personal loan from a bank which knows you is usually the next best thing to an overdraft for this purpose, but if this is not available, once again a good place to look for details of other lenders who have a more sympathetic attitude towards aeroplanes is in Pilot, Flyer and the other aviation magazines, among their classified ad pages. AOPA UK also claims to have negotiated special rates for their members with certain loan companies. Once again however, the same caveat as before; this type of finance is not the cheapest around, so it is important to check very carefully what you are letting yourself in for before you enter into any binding contract to borrow in this way to help you to buy your aeroplane. You can very easily end up repaying vastly more than the basic cost of the aircraft, especially if the loan is taken out over a number of years. Even a reputable credit broker who advances you a loan of £25,000, which is to be paid back over a period of ten years, is likely to be demanding monthly repayments which will add up to a figure that is closer to £50,000 than £25,000 by the end of that ten year period. Best take an electronic calculator with you while you go to do your negotiations, and always be on your guard!

Pilots who buy their aircraft from a reputable second hand aircraft dealer, or are lucky enough to be buying a new machine direct from the manufacturer or the official distributor, will certainly find it well worth enquiring whether they have a financing scheme available. If the dealer or distributor has special arrangements made with a finance company this can often turn out to be an appreciably less expensive route to a loan for you as purchaser, than any direct approach you might make to an outside finance company. Since the seller usually will also earn some commission from the loan contract you enter into (in the same way as in the case of car dealers) it is also worth trying to use this fact to lever a keener price for the aircraft. If your purchase is being made directly from another private aircraft owner you will almost certainly have to arrange any necessary finance yourself. Just make sure you allow yourself sufficient time to arrange the least expensive type of loan that is available. Don't be too impetuous and end up saddling yourself with unnecessary extra expenses. Believe me, you will enjoy your new acquisition much more if you still have enough cash left over, after paying off the money lenders, to fly the aeroplane from time to time and maybe eat occasionally too.

Chapter 6
Tackling Something New

When was the last time you did something for the first time?

Flying as a PPL holder is chock full of opportunities for you to try novel and interesting things and as soon as you have mastered one of these there is always another waiting for you to tackle. Every new skill acquired, each new type of piloting experienced, all new challenges accepted and accomplished go a long way towards making a progressive pilot's life more exciting, more satisfying and more exhilarating. In this chapter I take you to have a look at just a few of the best cures that I know of that can prevent boredom creeping into any PPL holder's life.

Night Flying

It never seems to occur to many PPL holders that getting them a night qualification might be a good idea. Perhaps that is simply because most of them earn their licences without ever flying in the dark? And later in their flying lives they reckon that they've no intention of ever flying at night, so what's the point? Isn't night flying dangerous, especially in single engine aircraft, and aren't night qualifications difficult and expensive to obtain? So in the end they come to the conclusion that it is probably better just to leave flying in the dark to the professionals. Not many birds fly after sunset, so why the hell should you?

But none of that reasoning is necessarily true. A night qualification is one of the easiest and least expensive extras you can 'add on' to your PPL. Learning the basics of night flying extends your experience of airmanship in general and will help to make you a better pilot in daylight as well as in the dark. Flying at night is not inherently all that more risky than flying in daylight, always provided that the pilot in command is competent and is willing to take a few sensible precautions. Even if you have no intention of flying after sunset, a night qualification can be a very useful insurance against a flying expedition when you find yourself behind schedule (perhaps because of bad weather or delayed by passengers arriving late, or held up by air traffic control) and inadvertently find darkness creeping up on you before you can reach your destination.

Night flying brings new skills into play and rewards you with new sights and satisfaction.

Night flight can provide you with a marvellously enjoyable, almost ethereal experience, totally different from daylight piloting. It opens up new facets of airmanship, new sights and new satisfactions, as well as helping to eliminate that feeling of impending crisis if you are ever confronted in the air by a fast approaching sunset. This is altogether too good a thing to leave just to the professionals. Amateur pilots are perfectly capable of tackling darkness in a professional manner too.

With the exception of flight under the supervision of a qualified flying instructor, no PPL pilot may fly at night unless he or she has a night qualification. (This is the JAR equivalent of what was formerly known as a UK CAA Night Rating.) To obtain this qualification you must complete a course involving at least five hours of flying at night. This has to include at least three hours of flying instruction, of which at least one hour is to be of cross country navigation. You have also to carry out five solo take-offs and landings at night. Once you are qualified, then in order to carry passengers at night as a JAR PPL holder you must also meet the recency requirements. These are met provided you have carried out within the preceding 90 days, not fewer than three take-offs and three landings, as sole manipulator of the controls in an aircraft of the same type or class, with at least one of these take-offs and one of the landings having been done at night. Strangely enough, to qualify as a 'night' take-off or landing it is not sufficient that it takes place between 30 minutes after sunset and 30 minutes before sunrise (which is the definition of official 'night' for logbook entry purposes). The depression of the centre of the sun must, according to the Air Navigation Order, be not less than 12° below the horizon for your take-offs and landings to qualify for validation of your night rating. They don't always count, just because you do them while it's dark! And conversely, they do count even if you do them when there is a brilliant full moon making the night almost as bright as day.

Usefully, all this flying can also count towards the requirements for what might turn out to be your next step, the IMC or the instrument rating (IR). Once you qualify for your night qualification too, there is no need to undergo regular re-testing to renew it. You are thereafter entitled to fly at night, solo or (subject to the above recency requirements) whilst carrying passengers, any time you please. If you allow yourself to go beyond the 90 day period without carrying out sufficient take-offs and landings to meet the recency requirements you have only to make the number of take-offs and landings up to three, including that all important one done in the dark. You can as you wish do this either without, or under the supervision of, a flying instructor but it is illegal to take anyone with you during these flights, other than an instructor. Thereafter you are free to carry passengers at night again.

Within the UK, Channel Islands and Isle of Man airspace, no VFR flight is permitted at night (i.e. from 30 minutes after sunset until 30 minutes before sunrise) and so for flights at night, pilots must fly IFR. This does not mean that an instrument rating is necessary to fly at night. It means only that flight outside controlled airspace must be conducted within the limitations of the pilot's licence, which must be at least a PPL with a valid night qualification. The pilot must also comply with the minimum height rule (1,000 feet above the highest obstacle within 5nm of track) and, if operating above 3,000ft amsl, must fly in accordance with the quadrantal rule. VFR is not permitted within Class A airspace at any time, and if the night flight involves flying within a Control Zone that peculiar form of IFR clearance known as a Special VFR clearance must be requested from ATC.

It Can be Different in the Dark

Don't assume that as the holder of a night qualification you can automatically fly at night under similar regulations in all other countries. Despite the European harmonisation of regulations under JAR mentioned in Chapter 4, wide variations still exist in VFR night flying rules. Night VFR is not permitted at all in, for example, the Netherlands, Spain, Italy and Denmark. Special permission must be obtained to fly night VFR in Austria, Greece, Iceland and the Republic of Ireland. It is restricted to varying extents in Belgium, Luxembourg, France and Finland. Within Europe, it is only in the UK, Germany, Switzerland, Norway and Sweden, where you can be fairly certain of being able to exercise the privileges of your night qualification without too many restrictions. In fact in several of these countries you can fly VFR at night as well as during daylight hours. In the United States the FAA has never thought it either necessary or desirable to ban the world's largest GA population from flying VFR between sunset and sunrise.

Presumably the reason that the authorities in so many countries do ban or severely restrict night VFR is that they regard it as being inherently dangerous. But it is, in point of fact, no exotic adventure, no rash, uncalculated risk. There is, admittedly, always some risk of inadvertently flying into IMC in the dark. Clouds are much more difficult to spot at night than during the day but if at night the ground lights and stars all unexpectedly fade from sight; it is probably high time you executed that 180° safety turn to regain visual conditions. A thorough study of the forecast weather before night flying is always a must. The other big worry is of course engine failure, especially in a single engine aircraft. Aero engines are, on the whole, remarkably reliable beasts, but if the donkey ever did decide to die on you at night in a single, you would be the first to admit that it all suddenly becomes a great deal more stressful than in broad daylight. One fatalistic piece of 'advice' for such an occasion is to aim for a dark piece of terrain (so you would most probably be heading for open country or woodland and keeping clear of the collision hazard of buildings), then switch on your landing light when you reckon you are about a couple of hundred feet above the ground and, if you don't like what you see, just switch the light off again quickly and start praying.

Electrical failure too can put a great deal more additional pressure on you if it occurs at night than it is ever likely to do in daylight. Which is one more good reason for carrying not just the obligatory torch for map and instrument reading, but also spare batteries and a bulb or even better a complete spare torch? (It is much easier swapping torches than trying to swap a fiddly little bulb whilst flying an aeroplane through turbulent air in total darkness!)

Nocturnal Niceties

Flying at night can be a delightful experience. There are fewer aircraft in the air and those that are flying are easier to see with their colourful strobes, flashing beacons and navigation lights twinkling. The night air is frequently far smoother than by day, often devoid of thermal turbulence. Your aircraft often seems to slip silkily through the sky in a way you seldom otherwise enjoy. The view of an urban landscape at night can be unexpectedly beautiful, in contrast to its normally drab daytime appearance. Skeins of lights, mercury blue, tungsten white and sodium yellow, trace the lines of roads and streets with ribbons of vehicle headlights trickling past them. Shop lights, factory signs, floodlit sports grounds, advertisements and traffic lights all help transform even an ugly industrial landscape into something resembling fairyland.

Even a couple of thousand feet above the surface at night you are often clear of much of the dust and smoke that dulls the natural sparkle of the stars. Flight on a cloudless night can then provide an unforgettable spectacle of the starry heavens, each pinpoint of light shining with a clarity you seldom can see from ground level. A moonlit night too can provide a memorable flight; black hills etched against the luminescent sky, silvery lakes against the dark background of open country and maybe breaking waves sparkling in the lunar light along a coastline. Night flying is for lovers, for poets and all romantics.

Numerous books are available on the subject of night flying, covering the techniques of navigation at night, approach and runway lighting, taxiing techniques and the physiology of night flying. It wouldn't be a bad idea for you to get hold of one of these and read it before embarking on your course for the night qualification. The qualification itself will certainly more than adequately reward you for the relatively small effort and expense that is involved in adding it to your PPL.

The Instrument Meteorological Conditions (IMC) Rating

As a first aim after achieving their PPL many enterprising private pilots in the UK head for an Instrument Meteorological Conditions (IMC) Rating. The requirements for this are fairly stringent but not really off putting. The achievement of an IMC rating is an indication that you have mastered a great deal of the advanced techniques of airmanship involved in flying light aircraft. The reward you get as the holder of a PPL with an IMC rating is that you can legally continue flying in weather conditions that are poorer, in terms of cloud base and visibility, than the PPL holder without an IMC rating is allowed to penetrate. PPL holders with an IMC rating are, subject to certain specified minima, permitted to fly under IMC within Class D, E, F and G airspace. Unfortunately, the IMC rating is valid only within UK airspace. Across the Channel or the Irish Sea (except in the airspace above Northern Ireland) the holder of a PPL may not exercise the privileges of his or her IMC rating as this is not an internationally recognised rating.

When you are heading towards an Instrument or IMC rating you soon develop an enhanced degree of interest in the instrument panel and avionics of your aircraft, in this case a Grumman AA 5 Traveller.

The advantages of having an IMC rating whilst flying within UK airspace are significant, but they are still a long way below those of a full instrument rating. PPL pilots without an IMC rating are prohibited from flying outside controlled airspace when the visibility is less than 3km; IMC rated PPL pilots can fly outside controlled airspace down to zero visibility. Compared with the non-IMC rated PPL, the pilot with a valid IMC rating can also fly under IFR within Class D Airspace subject to certain specified minima. These limitations do tend to alter from time to time and so, rather than spell out the current ones here, when future readers will probably find them misleading, I recommend you always to refer to the latest information that is available in publications such as the UK Air Pilot, LASORS, current AICs, the ANO and elsewhere.

Before starting the course for an IMC rating a new PPL pilot must have flown at least 25 hours (which has to include a minimum of ten hours pilot in command and five hours cross-country flight) since applying for the PPL. To qualify for the IMC rating, a specified course which includes 15 hours of instrument flying (of which two may be conducted in a CAA approved simulator) must be completed. The associated ground study involves at least 20 hours of instruction covering physiological factors, flight instruments, the Aeronautical Information Service, flight planning and the privileges associated with the IMC rating. Finally a flight test and ground examination has to be passed. An IMC rating remains valid for 25 months, after which it can be renewed by issue of a certificate of competence on completion of a renewal flight test. The requirements involved are all detailed in LASORS and this publication really is required reading for any private pilot who is contemplating acquiring an IMC rating.

Advantages of the IMC Rating

Quite apart from its usefulness in allowing a PPL holder to stay legal, within the UK at least, in weather conditions poorer than those in which unrated private pilots are permitted to fly, an IMC rating gives you useful reassurance of your ability to fly accurately on instruments and to carry out a safe approach and landing using a an approach procedure or precision instrument landing system. It is an excellent confirmation of your ability to fly reasonably competently on instruments and it is a very useful insurance against being caught out by adverse weather conditions. Unfortunately because it is not valid anywhere else in Europe other than the UK it doesn't really give you any particularly significant advantages over the non IMC PPL holder while flying outside the UK. It is, none the less, still a very useful and satisfying rating to acquire, either for its own sake or as a stepping stone towards the full IR.

The Instrument Rating (IR)

The full instrument rating is both a challenging and an expensive step for any private pilot to take but it is, in the opinion of many businessmen pilots, a step that is essential unless you are prepared to limit the flying you do with your PPL solely to recreational flights or to very limited business use. The reason for this thinking is simple. Weather conditions in the British Isles, and throughout much of continental Europe, are such that it is seldom possible to make a cross country flight of any significant length and still be reasonably certain of being able to fly back again legally, keeping to your planned schedule, in weather conditions that comply with VFR. It is a sad fact that, in an effort to maintain a planned schedule, and without giving sufficient consideration to the prevailing weather conditions, private pilots without instrument ratings (and many of their passengers) have fallen victim to the fatal ailment sometimes referred to as 'get-home-it-is'. The very best antidote for this nasty affliction is simply to have sufficient willpower to stay safely on the ground until conditions improve. Sadly, this simple remedy can sometimes have awkward side effects on business schedules or on personal plans. A less constricting cure for the malady is an adequate injection of instrument flying training. This, in conjunction with a suitably equipped aircraft, can turn 'get-home-it-is' into a relatively innocuous disease, but it still does remain literally life threatening to inexperienced pilots (including these with valid Instrument Ratings) who take the risk of flying in weather that is so bad that more experienced IR qualified pilots would remain on the ground.

Unfortunately, the JAA instrument rating is both expensive and difficult to achieve, especially for PPL pilots who are able to fly only a limited number of hours annually. Before committing yourself to start your training for an IR, desirable as it may be in terms of safety in every aspect of the flying you do, it is best for you first to analyse exactly how the cost/benefit ratio would work out in your own circumstances. After a couple of experiences of sitting at some foreign airfield, socked in by bad weather and burning with jealousy at the clever dicks who simply file IFR, fire up their engines and vanish through the layers of low cloud and rain, it is very tempting to decide you absolutely must head for an IR of your own. Life seems so much simpler for those other pilots, not having to phone home or e-mail the office to explain the situation, not running up unwanted hotel bills and aircraft parking charges. If you are ultimately aiming to qualify for a commercial licence then there is no question about it at all. An IR is an essential. If you are planning to use an aircraft regularly for business it is, to say the least, highly desirable. If you fly only for pleasure you may well find that, even after it becomes perfectly legal for you to fly in instrument conditions, your new instrument rating is still going to be very under-utilised. For a whole variety of reasons, some of which are discussed below, many instrument rated private pilots often end up doing very little instrument flying at all.

Even so, the effort in self improvement that you are involved in while qualifying for your instrument rating will certainly not prove to have been in vain. An IR opens up all sorts of other opportunities, enabling you to fly airways in UK airspace (an activity incidentally, that you can undertake without any instrument qualification in many other parts of the world) gaining you valuable experience in controlled airspace operations, giving you an invaluable 'escape route' in case the weather clamps down on you unexpectedly, and generally increasing your flying experience and (hopefully) your weather wisdom. What an IR does not always do for you (contrary to the ideas nurtured by many non instrument rated pilots) is make your flying simpler. It can at times actually make it considerably more complicated. Filing IFR may let you fly through clouds and along airways but it also means you have to ask for clearances to depart, to alter your routing and to change your cruising altitude. You lose much of the spontaneity that makes VFR flying so enjoyable. Nor does an IR make you magically independent of weather.

Even airliners have to cancel occasionally, and they have certain advantages over you, like two pilots on the flight deck who are in regular flying practice, weather radar, and superior avionics to yours, de-icing equipment, and ground support and so on.

An IR Doesn't Make You Immune

If you normally pilot a typical single or twin engine light aeroplane your aircraft is unlikely to be cleared for flight in known icing conditions. This cuts down considerably on cloud flying, especially (but not only) during the winter months. Even if you add an IR to your PPL this doesn't mean the end of weather imposed flight cancellations, even when there is no danger of encountering icing conditions. You still have weather minima; considerably lower than for the pilot without an IR admittedly, but still high enough for you to be occasionally defeated by really grotty visibility or an awkwardly low cloud base. And an IR clipped to your PPL will very definitely not guarantee you safe passage through a thunderstorm. What your IR does bring with it is a certainty that you are going to be called upon to make some very vital decisions. As a single pilot in a light aircraft with probably only limited avionics and instrumentation and no de-icing equipment, what degree of nasty weather are you prepared to tackle? You may have an IR in your pocket but are you not perhaps a little short of recent instrument flying experience? That's a point you should always factor into your go/no go decision. When, as is often the case, the weather situation is not clear cut, when the fog might, or then again might not, burn off, when the ceilings at the destination are hovering around your minima, the IR pilot can have quite a stressful time coming to a sensible decision. It can all be a whole lot more difficult for you than for the non-instrument rated PPL pilot alongside you.

Although even a full Instrument Rating doesn't make you immune to bad meteorological conditions, the training involved in obtaining even an IMC rating should enable you to cope more confidently with difficult flying weather.

Weighing the Cost

Think back over the last couple of years of your flying. How many times have you been held up by weather? How many times would you like to have flown but couldn't, simply because you were not instrument rated? How important these 'lost' flights, time delays and associated costs actually were to you, should give you at least a guide as to whether you should sign up for that IR course. If this approach seems to give you a green light, sit down next and add up the cost of the course at a CAA approved flying school. It involves at least 50 hours flying for an IR valid in single engine aircraft, or 55 hours if you want a Multi Engine Pilot (MEP) IR for multi engine aircraft. (Currently this could cost you anything from £10,000 to £15,000). Don't forget then to add the costs of getting to and from wherever you will be doing the training, any accommodation expenses, plus the cost of the time you will need to be away from work etc. Then there is the cost of the CAA Flight Examiner's Flight Test (currently well over £700) and that of getting to Gatwick to sit the ground examinations which last about a day and a half and so involve you in having more time off work.

You, as a PPL pilot, have to meet precisely the same standards as any other CPL or ATPL applicant for an instrument rating. You are also required to go through the same regular re-testing to maintain the validity of your hard won Instrument Rating. Financially, there are further implications too. Is the aeroplane you intend flying already correctly equipped and certified for IFR? If not, it might cost you quite a tidy sum to bring it up to standard, or considerably more for you to rent an aeroplane that is fully IFR equipped. And of course, to make any real use of your IR you will need to subscribe to the appropriate Jeppesen or Aerad instrument charts and guides. These are quite a bit more expensive than the VFR flight guide and the half-million ICAO charts which, although still required, will no longer be sufficient for you as an instrument rated pilot.

If an honest appraisal of the financial situation persuades you that an IR is not for you, there is no need to be ashamed about it or to start making excuses. There are a multitude of other things still open for you to do with your PPL, and in some ways a decision not to go for an IR could well leave you with a more relaxed flying lifestyle. But if you can afford to become instrument rated, and the cost/benefit analysis indicates that in your case it is worth doing so, and then you should certainly go for it. You then will be transformed into that pilot who can fly out of a sodden, dingy, grey airfield and leave the VFR pilots sitting impatiently waiting for a weather clearance. It is now you who will be able to spend the night at home with your family instead of in the airfield motel. You can experience the pleasure of leaving a miserable day on the ground and breaking out into sparkling sunshine a few thousand feet above ordinary mortals. You can enjoy the immense satisfaction of seeing the runway lights emerging from the overcast a few hundred feet below and ahead of you, just where the instruments told you they were going to be. You will have gained immeasurably in experience and competence from your extra training and that is certainly going to have beneficial effects on many other aspects of your flying.

If your cash calculations show that an IR is likely to fit in with your flying lifestyle then that becomes the point where you have to make your first go/no go decision. Whilst thinking of all the benefits that flying by instruments might bring, remember too what it is going to cost you in study, effort and hard cash before you finally make up your mind that this really is your thing.

Bigger, Faster and More Complex

Unless you happen to be a hopeless romantic about flying you have to agree that the real purpose of an aeroplane is to move people and goods around the place at a reasonable speed. Eventually (although some pilots never seem to reach this stage and others take ages to get there) you will probably realise that the leisurely speeds achieved by training and basic touring aircraft such as Cessna Skyhawks, Grumman Cheetahs and Piper Warriors, are less than ideal for much of the flying you would like to do. Aircraft like these which once seemed to you to be a real handful to cope with, gradually begin to feel unexciting and, perhaps more importantly, much too slow. The legs and wheels just hanging out there in the breeze begin to annoy you. You enviously watch other pilots take-off in lean, mean machines that tuck their undercarriages away out of sight as soon as they are off the ground and benefit thereafter from increased speed, climb, and general efficiency. These are the signs that show you are beginning to suffer from the high performance syndrome.

The Beechcraft Bonanza is typical of the faster and more complex single engine aeroplanes onto which many pilots who were trained on basic two or four seat training aircraft aim to progress.

Unless you are getting rather long in the tooth (or your basic training was rather unusual for the present day) you probably learned to fly on single engine light aircraft with fixed pitch propellers and fixed tricycle undercarriages. The trainers you used were very probably powered by piston engines that delivered not much more than 100 or 150hp at the most. But until recently a PPL was a licence to pilot any aircraft of the type or group specified in your aircraft rating and for a private pilot the Group A rating specified all single-engine aeroplanes not exceeding 5,700kg maximum total weight authorised. A car driver who has just passed a driving test in a Ford Fiesta can, quite legally, hop into a Ferrari Testarossa and drive off in it. Similarly you, as holder of a brand-new JAA PPL, would until quite recently have been legally entitled to clamber into the cockpit of a Piper Malibu, or even a Supermarine Spitfire, and try to fly off in it. All you would have had to do first would have been wealthy enough to buy one, because that would probably be a whole lot easier than finding an owner of such an aircraft who was crazy enough to let you fly it. It has to be said too, that our hypothetical Ferrari driver would be much more likely to survive his ton up driving experience unscathed than you would have been to live to tell the tale of your high performance airborne adventure.

Until the introduction by the UK CAA of differences training for complex aircraft it would have been perfectly legal (if seriously unwise) for a newly-fledged PPL holder to get into the cockpit of a Supermarine Spitfire like this and try to pilot it.

That is one reason why what is known as 'differences training' has been brought into being by the European authorities. The FAA in the United States had instituted a requirement back in 1973 that all pilots wanting to fly 'high performance' aircraft must take a one-time conversion course before they were permitted to fly an aircraft with either more than 200 horsepower, or a retractable undercarriage, controllable propeller and flaps. At one time training in either a 'high performance' or a 'complex' aircraft was enough to qualify FAA licenced pilots to qualify for a high performance endorsement, but the current regulations separately and specifically define these two terms. A complex airplane is one with retractable landing gear, flaps, and a controllable pitch propeller. A high performance airplane is one with an engine of more than 200 horsepower. Even though the training requirements are similar for both classifications, the FAA now says that meeting the requirements for one classification no longer meets the requirements for the other.

Under JAR rules (which also now apply to pilots with the old JAA PPL) the holder of a single engine or multi engine piston aeroplanes (land) class rating must undergo additional 'differences training' before acting as pilot in command of any aeroplane which has a variable pitch propeller, or retractable undercarriage, or turbo/supercharged engine(s), or cabin pressurisation, or has a tail wheel configuration, or any combination of more than one of these. Pilots who have logged PIC time on any of these variants of aeroplane can claim 'grandfather rights' and are permitted to fly them without the need to undergo any formal 'differences training'. Just the same, you should remember that even aircraft within the same class can exhibit very different flying characteristics, and you would be well advised always to seek proper instruction before your first flight in a type of aircraft that is new to you. One could say that the authorities on both sides of the Atlantic have decided that it is just not possible to regulate good judgement completely into aviation, and that it is always better to rely on the common sense of the pilots involved. They also rely to some extent on the insurance underwriters who are justifiably reluctant to cover pilots whose only experience is of flying aircraft like basic two seat Cessna's, when they want to take over as pilots in command of more sophisticated aeroplanes. Almost invariably the insurers insist on being satisfied that such pilots have first undergone adequate supervised conversion training.

Making Conversions

So, if and when you do decide to head for more power, more aerodynamic efficiency or probably both together, what sort of conversion training should you be looking for? Most reasonably competent pilots could probably rely on their basic piloting instinct to cope with a moderate increase above the horsepower they have been accustomed to, if that is the only change. They, and you, could quickly adjust to factors like the aircraft's greater tendency to swing as you take-off and to the way it climbs more quickly and generally makes everything happen a little more rapidly than you were previously accustomed to. Moving to an aircraft that has something more than just a few extra horses to pull it along, perhaps one that also has a retractable undercarriage, constant-speed propeller and perhaps a fuel-injected engine, is a different matter entirely. It makes eminently good sense, as well as being a mandatory requirement, for you to get some 'differences' training for it.

Variable-Pitch Propellers

With no training or experience of constant-speed propeller operation it is not at all difficult, even for a pilot with many hours of fixed pitch prop flying in the log book, to inflict some potentially expensive loads on the innards of the engine. This type of prop can be regarded as acting in a manner similar to the gearbox of a car. Select fine pitch (or low gear) and you get high RPM for take-off. Changing into a 'second gear' provides a suitable setting for climbing, and coarse pitch (high gear) is what should normally be used for economical cruising with the engine turning at low RPM. Trying to pull away at full throttle from slow speed in a car with top or overdrive gear selected, can result in the engine 'lugging' and 'pinking' and gives pretty lamentable performance. Trying to fly an aircraft at low airspeed with coarse pitch and full throttle you don't hear the pinking, but it (and the resulting damage to the engine) is still liable to be taking place and the performance is equally awful. Before each reduction of RPM (coarser pitch selection)

A constant speed propeller is essential to obtain optimum performance form a powerful piston engine like this radial in a Yak.

the throttle, which is still the power control, must be moved to a lower power setting so that the slower revving engine will not be 'lugging' with the throttle too wide open. To ensure that the engine is ready to respond to full throttle in the event of an overshoot from a balked landing, the propeller control must always be in the fine (high RPM) position before landing.

Rather than simply trying to memorise blindly which it is of the pitch and throttle levers you should move first when increasing and when decreasing power (rev up; throttle back) it is far better to take a bit of time to understand what each lever does and how this affects the workings of the engine. There are many good textbooks on the subject and it is rather too involved to go into in detail in a book of this nature. It is however worth mentioning one advantage that a real understanding of this subject should bring for you. It should help to dispel from your mind one of aviation's many myths; the one about 'squaring' the engine settings. Put about by many instructors who are either trying to make life over simple for their students, or who (less charitably) have probably never troubled to learn the subject thoroughly themselves, this is the idea that you must never have the manifold pressure (measured in inches of mercury) exceeding the RPM (measured in hundreds of RPM). They affirm that the ideal situation is always to set the throttle to give for example 27 inches manifold pressure when the revs are 2700 (for take-off), 25 'squared' for the climb and perhaps 23 'squared' in the cruise. Which is sheer nonsense! It is difficult to understand where this myth originated since, as any engineer will confirm, manifold pressure and engine RPM are like chalk and cheese, apples and oranges. Some instructors, and a whole lot of experienced pilots of high performance aircraft, even go so far as to suggest that if the inches of mercury ever do exceed the hundreds of RPM, you are over boosting the engine and it is liable to disintegrate. The fact is that with a normally aspirated engine you simply cannot over boost it. Such engines cannot use any pressure other than ambient atmospheric pressure to bring air into the cylinders. Aircraft manuals and POHs simply don't use the term 'over boost'. Many in fact list normal approved ranges of manifold pressure and RPM settings which include such combinations as 25 inches and 2100 RPM. It is only if you are willing to learn how to handle these engine control levers correctly that you will be able to maximise the performance, and really justify the extra cost involved in flying high performance aircraft. Manufacturers who write these handbooks generally know more about their aircraft and engines than self appointed clubroom 'experts' or even instructors who have been too idle to read the manuals so that they can teach students correctly. The moral of this is, once again, always to read, learn and digest the information in the POH or aircraft manual and not to accept as gospel everything that comes out of an instructor's mouth.

Remember the Greens

In a high performance aircraft one omission from you're before landing checks could easily result in a financially disastrous wheels up contact with the runway. It is all too easy, following years of mumbling the vaguely amusing 'undercarriage down and welded' as part of the pre-landing check in a simple aircraft, to absent mindedly mumble the same phrase when you are flying a retractable. Not all of these are considerate enough to warn you automatically of your oversight in the convenient way the Piper Arrow kindly does. Folding legs and wheels come in a multiplicity of different designs. Some, such as Mooneys, Bonanzas and the Comanche, use electric motors and reduction gearing to operate the undercarriage. The majority, however, use hydraulic power for this job.

Until you fly aeroplanes with constant-speed propellers you never have to learn the importance of manifold pressure.

Some older types of aircraft use engine-driven hydraulic pumps but the most popular system in current designs is electro hydraulic. The Piper Arrow is typical of these. It has a power pack located under the rear seats. This comprises an electric motor coupled to a hydraulic pump and a reservoir of hydraulic oil. After take-off, moving the gear switch from down to up once you have established a positive rate of climb, earths one side of the electric motor's relay. The current coming to the other side from the aircraft main power bus bar has first to pass through a couple of circuit breakers. One of these is designed so that no current is allowed to pass any time there is any weight on the undercarriage; this prevents inadvertent retraction whilst the aircraft is on the ground. The other is controlled by a hydraulic pressure switch which allows current to flow if the system pressure drops below about 1,000 psi and cuts it off if it exceeds about 1,500 psi. The purpose behind this is to let the motor run and the pump force oil into the cylinders that retract the undercarriage, until all three legs and wheels are safely tucked away. The system pressure will then rise as the motor pump unit tries to push more oil into the now stationary system and, when pressure exceeds 1,500 psi, this second pressure switch cuts the motor out. If the pressure later falls below the 1,000 psi figure it automatically switches itself on again for long enough to build up pressure again, ensuring that the wheels stay safely in place. The Gear Down switch more or less reverses the process, with the electric motor and pump turning in the other direction. It doesn't have to work quite so hard since gravity lends a hand in this direction. The 'Gear Unsafe' or red/green lights are coupled to micro switches in the undercarriage system.

When a retractable undercarriage machine like this Cessna 177RG cleverly tucks its wheels away out of sight and out of the airstream it makes a huge improvement to the aircraft's looks as well as its performance.

Most retractables also have an emergency undercarriage lowering system available, in case there is ever a failure of the normal system. These vary in operation, and are fortunately not all that often used, but you should always ensure that you are familiar with precisely how the one fitted to the aircraft you are flying does operate. You can never be sure just when you might urgently need the knowledge. A failure usually means that the aircraft is turned into a fixed gear model, because not many manufacturers explain how to use any form of emergency retraction, only extension. Most Cessna systems do in fact permit emergency retraction, although the handbooks don't usually explain how to use them for this purpose. After all, once you have got a defective undercarriage down into place for the landing, it doesn't seem altogether a bad idea just to leave it there rather than tempt fate, would you not agree?

Just like the flaps (and indeed the aircraft themselves) retractable undercarriages have limiting speeds of their own. These are determined by several factors, the main one often being the strength of the undercarriage doors and their ability to stay attached to the airframe. Vlo is the maximum speed at which the landing gear may be raised or lowered and on some aircraft another slightly higher speed is quoted, Vle which is the maximum speed you may fly with the landing gear locked down in the extended position. Some models also have a maximum gear retraction speed, lower than the Vlo. Taking the Piper Arrow as an example again, you can lower the wheels at the Vlo of 133 knots, but the handbook quotes 111 knots as the maximum airspeed for retraction of the undercarriage. Whichever type you are flying, these are speeds you must know. Without them at your fingertips you are putting the structural integrity of the aircraft at risk.

If the aircraft's engine is fuel injected, and until now you've always flown carburettor types, you might end up with nothing worse than a flat battery and a red face when you discover you have no idea how to get the thing to start; at least that might save you from some other embarrassments! High performance aeroplanes also tend to be fitted with avionics stacks that are a bit more comprehensive than training aircraft usually have. It is well worth spending some time on the ground studying the knobs and switches associated with these before even thinking about flying. Trying to work out in the air how to change from VHF Box 1 to Box 2, or how to set a particular code or to 'squawk Ident' on a transponder you aren't familiar with are problems you can do without. This sort of trivial but mind occupying thing can quickly get inexperienced pilots into trouble while scudding through the air at a speed that is appreciably faster than they are accustomed to.

Each Step Seems Smaller

Moving from a Cessna 152 to a 172 Skyhawk involves comparatively small changes in techniques and procedures; the change from the 172 to a 177RG Cardinal requires considerably more preparation. However, after you have made one such transition, whether to a Cardinal RG, a Beech Bonanza, Piper Arrow, TB-20 Trinidad or a SIAI -Marchetti SF-260, then you should have developed the basic background knowledge that will allow you to convert more easily to other similar (or even quite different) high-performance or complex aircraft. All you should need to do then is simply to use your own intelligence and common sense and to study the appropriate aircraft manuals thoroughly before you get into the cockpit.

Familiarity Breeds Competence

Studying the manual is an important prerequisite for any conversion onto any new type; it is especially important when you are making that big step to your first high-performance machine. Read the handbook, memorise it as far as you can, sleep with the damn thing, get someone to quiz you on it until you know the systems, performance, limitations, emergency procedures and all the rest that there is to know about it. Time spent on the ground doing this, whether at home or in the classroom, is cheap; time spent airborne learning the same stuff in the cockpit can work out pretty expensive. Knowing in advance the different procedures that have to be used to start a cold engine and a hot one can save embarrassment. Knowing before you ever touch the controls how to operate the emergency landing gear extension system can save more than that.

Keeping the fuel tanks in balance is no problem in a Cessna 152; it can be much more complicated, and is also much more important, in many other types. Just because you have more power up front still doesn't necessarily mean you can now carry four up, plus full tanks and baggage, without the aircraft going outside its weight and balance limits. Learn what these limits are for the new type you are going to fly. If this is the first time you have met a constant-speed propeller that is another whole field of study for you to absorb before you even touch either the throttle or the pitch lever. Remember which of them it is you do move first, and why.

The basic rule is a simple one. Know your aeroplane. Know what to expect, know what to do if something unexpected happens. It is all that much easier too, if you take the trouble to understand why things work the way they do. This is not the book to explain fully the interaction between cylinder pressure and propeller pitch, what makes a fuel injected engine start differently from the carburettor types you are probably more used to, why there are different maximum speeds for retracting and extending the undercarriage. There are plenty of good textbooks that will explain these matters to you. Take the trouble to read and understand them, ensure you have extracted all there is to know from the aircraft's own handbook, and you should approach your first flight in the high performance aeroplane with a great deal more confidence. You should also succeed in flying it a great deal more competently than the know all who mutters something about them all being much the same as, he or she climbs into the cockpit and starts the slow and expensive job of learning everything from scratch in the air, the hard way. Know your aeroplane thoroughly on the ground before you start getting to know how it performs in the air.

During my own conversion to the first high performance type I flew, my instructor insisted that I sit in the cockpit with my eyes blindfolded and reach out instantaneously to touch or point to each control or instrument the moment he named it. Flap lever; oil temperature; fire extinguisher; VHF radio; landing lamp; rudder trim; turn and slip; hood release. I can still hear his litany and more than forty years after the last time I ever flew one of them, I can still remember where most of these items are in the cockpit of a North American Harvard!

Taking to the Air

Once you have all these ground study preliminaries safely out of the way, it is time to start making your transition to a high performance aircraft actually in the air. Keeping up with the higher speed of the new type is a common problem for the tyro pilot; everything seems to be happening a lot quicker than it used to do in a simpler, slower type like a Diamond Katana, Piper Tomahawk or Robin DR400. You must always remember that it is you who are flying the aeroplane. Don't ever begin to let it fly you. The moment you start getting the uncomfortable feeling that the aeroplane is beginning to try to take control is the moment to stop, hand over to the instructor if necessary, get a grip of the situation and start off from the beginning again. In some ways, once you get used to them, high performance aircraft are actually easier to fly than the lighter types you have been used to because of their heavier wing loading which tends to make them more stable. But that can be a drawback too, as it gives them a tendency to fly themselves straight into the ground if you allow yourself get behind the aeroplane on the approach. It also gives many of these more complex aircraft very different stall characteristics from the ones you have grown used to during your initial training. Some, especially when in the flaps extended and undercarriage-down landing configuration, have the particularly nasty habit of giving the pilot virtually no buffeting, or any other aerodynamic stall warning at all, before everything suddenly goes horribly pear shaped.

Circuits are the Hardest Bits

It is while you are flying circuits that the extra work load and higher performance of these machines might first tend to make you feel that the aeroplane is getting ahead of you. You need more rudder to keep straight on take-off due to the extra engine torque. Then there is the undercarriage to be retracted and, immediately after that, it takes you a few seconds longer to make the adjustment to climb power, since there are now two control levers to be looked after instead of just the one you are more accustomed to handling. Meantime, of course, the new aeroplanes higher rate of climb means you are up to circuit height appreciably sooner than you have been in the habit of reaching it in a more leisurely aeroplane. The downwind leg should take about the same time as usual, because you should reduce power (two controls again) to adjust your speed to keep pace with trainers in the circuit. That slower downwind helps too, because there are a few extra items (such as the little matter of lowering the wheels) to include in the pre-landing checks checks. I still find the old BUMPFFHH a good mnemonic for a downwind checklist, well suited to most aircraft. Brakes off; Undercarriage down; Mixture fully rich; Prop pitch set to fine (high revs) unless for noise considerations you prefer to leave that to short final; Flaps set appropriately; Fuel on correct tank with booster pump on; Hood locked and Harness tight. The next power reduction, probably to about 10 or 12 inches of manifold pressure, follows quickly, and then base leg, where you must check that the green lights really are indicating that the wheels are down and locked, and check the speed is at the book figure for approach. If it isn't, then now is the time to do what's needed to get it there. On final approach you'll need full flap to reduce your speed to 1.3Vso and your power setting should be adequate to achieve a stabilised approach with a sink speed of no more than 500 feet per minute. More than that and the higher wing loading are liable to make the aeroplane fail to respond when you try to flare and it will then probably thump down hard onto the runway. This type of aircraft is seldom flown power off on the approach because the increased wing loading would make a glide approach very much shorter and steeper than a similar approach on a simple touring or training aircraft.

Getting Checked Out

The first time you make the transition to a high-performance single engine aeroplane it is well worth spending several hours in general handling and circuit work, accompanied by a pilot (preferably an instructor) who is experienced on the type. The time to discontinue the conversion training will become obvious to you. It doesn't arrive until you know for a fact that you can keep comfortably ahead of the aeroplane under all circumstances. If you haven't learned how to stay ahead of the machine you are supposed to be controlling, you really still amount to little more than the proverbial accident waiting for somewhere to happen. While converting to a high performance aircraft you are, of course, improving your general airmanship and flying skills for simpler aircraft at the same time. And when the time comes to move on to cope with a different type of high performance aeroplane; even though you shouldn't require anything like as much difference training or conversion, it is still a wise move to arrange for another checkout flight or two. This should help to ensure that you become familiar with any particular quirks that other aeroplane may have before you set off to fly it on your own. Much better than being surprised by them, up in the air, while you have nobody else alongside to help you cope with them. Flying high-performance aircraft is not necessarily an end in itself. All knowledge is cumulative and what you have learned in converting does force you to think farther ahead simply because everything is happening that much faster. This will be of enormous help to you later if you decide to go on to learn to fly multi engine aircraft or to train for an instrument rating.

Taming Taildraggers

Not until several years after World War 2 ended did many pilots do their primary training on anything other than tail wheel aircraft. After initial training on Tiger Moths, Magisters, Cornells or Piper Cubs, some WW2 pilots had to convert onto tricycle gear aircraft like the Airacobra, Mitchell, Albemarle, Liberator or Lightning (P-38 Lockheed variety, that was) but it wasn't until jet fighters like the Messerschmitt 262 Schwalbe, Gloster Meteor and de Havilland Vampire came along that nose wheel aircraft began to appear in larger numbers.

Post war basic training continued mainly on Piper Cubs and Pacers, Cessna 140s, Tiger Moths, Austers, Chipmunks and similar tail wheel types. Until Piper brought out the nose wheel version of the Pacer in 1951, and called it the Tripacer, about the only nose wheel light aircraft seen in any numbers had been the Ercoupe. The Tripacer sold like hot cakes and suddenly everyone found out what they had been missing. Cessna soon caught on to the idea of tricycle gear light aircraft; the result was the 1955 Cessna 172, closely followed by the Cessna 182. With the notable exceptions of the Tipsy Nipper, Bolkow Junior and Rallye, European light plane manufacturers remained loyal to tail wheels until nearly the end of the 1950s, but since that era, more and more pilots have learned to fly without ever experiencing the trials and tribulations of pulling off a smooth, neat, three-point landing in a tail wheel aircraft. Nowadays a light aircraft with its nose in the air and tail on the ground looks a little odd, something of an anachronism, and a sort of mystique has grown up around these oddball machines.

Not by any means all tail-draggers are veteran or vintage classic aeroplanes. Quite a few like this Aviat Husky, sometimes called "a Piper Cub for the 21st century," are in current production.

Nose wheel trained pilots are sometimes told they'll never be real pilots until they have learned to cope with one of these relics from a bygone age. Some accept the challenge and find out that they do indeed have quite a lot new to learn. Others retort, 'Why should I bother with a tail wheel aircraft? What possible advantage is there in that old-fashioned idea?' And in a way they are quite correct. Tail dragger aficionados will run out of reasons after saying that tail draggers are lighter, less draggy, give better prop clearance and are generally better for short, rough strips. They keep quiet about the swing on take-off, poor forward visibility on the ground, difficulty of consistently landing smoothly and the always lurking danger of a ground loop. But they still love their aircraft, the same way other folk love a 35 millimetre film camera instead of an automatic digital one, a fountain pen instead of a ballpoint, a car with a manual gearbox rather than an automatic transmission.

After you master the technique of piloting tail wheel aeroplanes you have the chance to add a whole range of interesting vintage types to your log book, such as a de Havilland Moth like this, some Austers...

... or a handsome Stearman biplane

Learning to cope with a tail dragger is still a very worthwhile extension of any pilot's skill and one that can be accomplished by any competent pilot without having to spend too much cash in the process. It is also a prerequisite for any pilot wanting to fly a Formula 1 racer, a biplane, almost any warbird, glider tug or crop-sprayer, many aerobatic aircraft, lots of LAA homebuilt types or any open cockpit aeroplane, since practically all of these are tail wheel designs. Pilots who can only cope with tricycle undercarriage aircraft severely limit the range of interesting aeroplanes they can fly. Before signing up for a few conversion lessons at one of the specialist schools or clubs offering instruction in Tiger Moths, Piper Cubs, Jodels, Stampes and even tail wheel Cessna 150 conversions (these organisations are all listed annually in for example Pilot Magazine's April Where to Fly Directory) it is as well to have an idea in advance of where the main differences lie.

In the tricycle undercarriage machines you have been flying up till now, the centre of gravity (C of G) is in front of the main undercarriage wheels. It obviously must be since, if it wasn't, the nose wheel would never stay on the ground! And equally obviously, a tail wheel aircraft's C of G has to be aft of the main wheels, otherwise it would come to rest with its prop digging into the turf instead of having its little tail wheel sitting safely on the tarmac. In the air this generally makes not the slightest bit of difference, but on the ground it certainly does. In a tricycle

The Ryan PT22 is another interesting tail-dragger type, more common in the US than in the UK

Perhaps an aerobatic machine like a Pitts special or this Starduster Too

machine, the forward C of G position helps to pull the aircraft back into line if it becomes displaced from a straight line while decelerating during the landing run. In the tail dragger it has exactly the opposite effect, pushing from behind the main gear and tending to swing the tail around in front of the main wheels - the classic ground loop situation. Taken to its extreme, if not corrected by a careful jab of opposite rudder or brake, closure of the throttle and holding the stick fully back and into the turn, the tail can swing around in a full circle, a wing and maybe a wheel may rise, then the tail can lift off the ground and (if the panic-stricken pilot slams on the anchors) the aircraft can even flip onto its back. All of which is most undignified, not to mention expensive. Yet after a little proper tuition it really becomes totally unnecessary, and is not all that likely to happen, despite all the hangar flying tales you hear about ground looping.

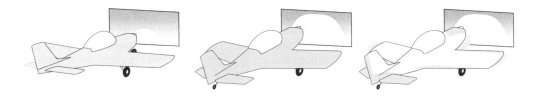

One disadvantage of tail wheel aircraft is the lack of forward vision on the ground. Here the pale blue area shows what the pilot of a typical tricycle undercarriage aircraft cannot see of the view ahead, while the yellow area shows the much larger area that is obscured to the pilot of a tail dragger.

Nose wheel aircraft are designed so that they are almost in flying attitude while on the ground, requiring only slight rotation at the correct speed in order to take-off. Tail draggers, on the other hand, have props that point at a distinct angle into the air whilst static, and they all require having their tails raised prior to take-off. This has the important consequence that, in addition to the slipstream effect and torque effect that tend to swing tricycle undercarriage aircraft on take-off, tail dragger pilots also have to contend with the gyroscopic effect (caused by tilting the rotating propeller as the tail comes up) and asymmetric blade effect (the result of the down going prop blade cutting into the air at a greater angle of attack than the up going one). The fact that all four of these forces happen to act in the same direction means that tail

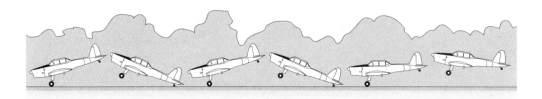

Tail draggers need more careful handing if you want to bring off consistently good landings. If instead of landing in the three point attitude, the machine touches down on its main wheels it is liable to catapult itself back into the air again, and go on repeating the process.

wheel aircraft have an appreciably greater tendency to swing on take-off. This is a swing to the left with clockwise rotating engines (all American ones) and to the right on those few aircraft fitted with counter clockwise rotating engines, mainly the older European manufactured ones like the Gipsy, Cirrus, Renault and so on.

In the heyday of tail wheel aircraft most flying took place from grass airfields and the duty runway always pointed more or less straight into wind. With no crosswinds to contend with, swings that led to ground loops were comparatively rare occurrences. The ability to cope with crosswind landings in a tail wheel aircraft is one sign of a well-trained pilot who has kept in good practice. The personal satisfaction obtained from being able to make consistently smooth and accurate three-point landings in a tail dragger, is just one of the many joys you can achieve from being a pilot. Landing tail high on the main wheels only, is another technique worth learning; it helps you cope with crosswinds and gusty conditions. If you were taught to fly on a tricycle undercarriage aeroplane you will undoubtedly have fond memories of the thrill you got from your first solo flight in it. You could well find that your first solo at the controls of a tail wheel aeroplane will give you just as much pleasure, and maybe even more satisfaction, when you conclude it with a sweet, smooth greaser of a three-point landing.

Having mastered the quirks of flying tail draggers you'll find that many new aspects of flying have opened up to you. As already mentioned, the best aerobatic aircraft tend to have tail wheels. So do many of the economical homebuilt aircraft and rugged types of aircraft that are generally the ones best suited to short strip operations. You will have the satisfaction of knowing that you have learned to fly the way every pilot had to learn throughout the first half century of powered flying. The tail wheel training and experience should have turned you into a more competent and a more confident pilot, even when you are piloting one of these newfangled things with the wheel at the sharp end that take much of the airmanship and half the fun out of landing in stiff crosswinds.

You will find that crosswind landings are trickier on tail-wheel aircraft than you are accustomed to when flying tricycle undercarriage aeroplanes, largely because they are flown at a larger angle of attack. Undercarriages with wider spaced main wheels are easier to keep straight after landing than narrow track ones. The distance between main wheels and tail wheel also plays a part; if the triangle shown here is long and sharp pointed, landings are easier to control than if it is short and stubby.

Techniques for Twins

In the United States one of the most popular additions to a private pilot licence is a multi engine rating. However, the same cannot be said for Europe in general. Differing costs of hire and ownership of twin engine aircraft, higher operating costs due to greedier fuel burn and landing charge penalties, tend to put even the smaller light twins out of reach of many European pilots, however desirable they might at first appear to be. None the less, the training involved in learning how to fly a multi engine aircraft is valuable experience and none of the techniques to be tackled are beyond the ability of any competent single-engine private pilot. Transition from single engine piloting to flying twins is, of course, an essential early step for any pilot making his or her way towards a commercial licence.

The Piper Seminole is one of the many light twins which are economical to rent or buy, but which lack sufficient power to have adequate safety margins should one engine fail.

Buying Safety?

On the face of things, a twin engine aircraft should be a safer machine for you to fly than a single, especially if much of your flying is to be done over the sea or inhospitable terrain. If the motor quits in a single, there is only one way to go, and that is down. In a twin, theoretically at least, the loss of one engine should be no big deal. The other engine will continue to power the aircraft as the pilot flies safely and happily on to a suitable place for landing. But to achieve this ideal state of affairs that pilot has to be properly trained, in current flying practice and on top of his or her job. Even then, things aren't always quite as straightforward as that. For a start several light twins are scarcely able to maintain height on one engine when heavily loaded, at high density altitude, or when in take-off or landing configuration. Unfortunately, most of the types that are likely to seem almost affordable for you, either to own or rent, fall into this category. This includes the Piper Seminole, Seneca I and Twin Comanche, the Beech Duchess, Grumman Cougar and a good few others. The pilot's operating handbook figures may tell a different story, quoting quite an impressive single engine service ceiling figure. What they don't usually make clear is that in order to climb up to that ceiling the aircraft must be 'clean' (with wheels and flaps up) atmospheric conditions must be normal and the dead engine's propeller must be feathered. With a wind milling engine, wheels and/or flaps out in the slipstream, a light twin with one engine out becomes a very inefficient flying machine. It is sometimes not much more, performance wise, than a glider with a mechanical source of noise out on one wing. A few of the smallest of the 'real' twin engine aircraft, which are actually capable of maintaining height and even climbing on one engine, are the Beech Baron, Cessna 310, Diamond Twin Star and the Piper Aztec.

The Thielert Diesel engines used in the Diamond DA-40 Twin Star give it a single engine climb performance of over 500 feet per minute at 12,000 feet.

The reason for the poor performance of some light twins with one engine isn't difficult to figure out. Supposing a hypothetical light twin requires 160 horsepower to fly straight and level in its minimum drag configuration, and that it is fitted with two 200 horsepower engines. It obviously has 240 spare horses to give it an impressive rate of climb and a useful cruising speed. If one of the engines fails, however, only 40 horsepower remains surplus to ideal minimum drag cruise requirements. That is quickly absorbed by a wind milling propeller and the hefty boot full of rudder you need to keep the aircraft straight, never mind any additional drag from wheels or flaps. So down it goes, not quite so rapidly perhaps as a single engine aircraft under similar circumstances, but inexorably down. And the twin pilot is left with a considerably increased workload compared with the single engine jockey after his or her motor quits. There is the asymmetric thrust of the remaining good engine to fight, the dead prop to feather, the systems of a more complex machine to cope with, and he or she is still confronted with an inevitable forced landing to be planned for at the same time. All this will give you some idea of why the multi engine qualification usually takes a competent single engine private pilot at least ten flying hours to complete (probably costing well over half what you paid for your entire PPL course). It shows too, how learning to fly twins will help to improve virtually any pilot's level of general airmanship.

A Cessna 310 costs approximately three times as much per hour to hire as a Cessna 152, so it behoves the multi engine student to minimise the time spent in the air learning things that could just as easily have been learned on the ground. For the sake of your bank balance, plan on spending at least six hours on serious book study before each hour in the cockpit. This study will cover the numerous V speeds that affect twins and not singles; Vmc, Vxse, Vyse and so on, what the 'critical engine' is, and the nuts and bolts of how you feather an engine (and how to be absolutely positive that it is the correct engine you are feathcring!). It would also be stupid to embark on twin training if you have never learned how to fly any single

With a multi-engine rating on your PPL you can consider piloting a real business twin such as the Cessna 340, complete with retractable undercarriage, constant speed propellers, pressurized cabin and de-icing equipment.

engine aircraft more complex than fixed undercarriage, fixed prop trainers and tourers. That way you end up paying around three times as much as you need to, just to learn how to cope with retractable gear, constant speed propellers and higher than normal wing loading. Best get all that behind you first whilst piloting a less expensive high performance single.

Single Engine Twin Training

A great deal of your training for the multi engine rating will be spent with only one of your engines delivering power. With both engines in good nick, apart from the slightly busier looking cockpit, you'll find there is precious little difference between piloting the twin and flying the single engine machines you are more accustomed to. There are differences though. One you will very quickly notice, is the lack of useful screws, rivets and scratch marks on the engine cowling ahead of you that you have been in the habit of using, perhaps subconsciously, to line up with the runway while you were coming in to land. Once they stuck an engine out on each wing most designers decided that a stubby little short nose was all you needed in front of the cockpit, and you just have to get used to the change in the view of the runway that this brings. The fact that the port engine looks bigger to you (ensconced as you are in the left hand seat) than the starboard, stuck away out there on the far wing, brings problems on landing too. Instinct sometimes tells you to try to even things up, the result of which can be you're swinging the aircraft to the left before touchdown, with an accompanying squeal of protest from the tyres. The greater curvature that the average twin's windshield has also tends to distort your picture of the runway; yet another small item you have to become accustomed to. And all these small items do tend to add up.

Only the first hour or so of your multi engine training will be spent getting the feel of the machine with both donkeys pulling; turning it, stalling it, feeling its slow flying characteristics and becoming accustomed to the new appearance of the world when it is no longer seen through that familiar propeller disc. From there on you will get to know in a very practical way the meaning of the word 'asymmetric'. Shortly thereafter you are liable to become very aware of a certain group of muscles in your legs after you have spent many happy hours having one engine or the other 'failed' on you. This exercise has just one aim; that is to enable you to develop the essential art of controlling a twin that has suddenly become a single engine aeroplane, just in case a twin that you are flying ever decides to pull that nasty trick on you. You will learn a new V speed here. Vmc, the minimum control speed which is, in effect, the lowest speed at which you can keep the nose straight with one engine out of action. This actually is a variable quantity, depending on the weight of the aircraft, which engine is out, whether the dead prop is feathered etc together with even a few intangible factors such as pilot technique. Twins bring lots of interesting new V speeds for you to learn. One of the most useful is Vse, the safe single engine speed, which is the slightly higher minimum speed that you should substitute for Vmc during engine failure training. This might help to reduce the too frequent accidents that have occurred when an over optimistic low Vmc has been used. One of the least useful must surely be Vxse; this is the best angle of climb speed when flying with one engine dead. Under what set of circumstances can you envisage trying to climb up to clear an obstacle in a twin which has only one fan turning?

During your multi engine training you'll spend a great deal of time with one of the engines of your twin stopped and its propeller feathered. Learing to cope with asymmetric forces following engine failure is a major part of this course.

Like most steps up the ladder of pilot proficiency, being able to exercise the privileges of a multi engine rating can bring a great deal of satisfaction. Perhaps not least among these is the satisfaction of being able to explain to those lesser mortals who are still restricted to single engine aircraft, just how easy the training all really was, how much more fun it is to pilot a big twin (like a Cougar or Twin Comanche perhaps?) and how much safer it is for all on board when you wing your way off to Guernsey or Rotterdam. (Cross your fingers as you make that claim, though; perhaps it would be better not to put that theory and your own new prowess to the test, especially if the aircraft happens to be anywhere near its maximum gross). There is something about flying a twin that does strange things to the ego of some pilots. These aircraft seem to give them a feeling of prestige that is quite liable to lead to a bad dose of over confidence. If you were born under one of the star signs that makes you susceptible to this, do your best to guard against it.

What really makes flying twins more fun is the very fact that they are more complicated than your average single. The feeling that you have the competence to master all these electric, hydraulic, fuel (up to six tanks to juggle on some) and other systems can give you a genuine feeling of satisfaction. There is possibly a slight danger that, as a new twin pilot, you may develop delusions of grandeur. These are sometimes fed by the tendency some Air Traffic Controllers have to accord priority to twins over single engine aircraft. It seems these controllers reckon that if you fly a twin you must be important. There is no doubt that, as and when you return to fly a humble single again, you are going to miss that feeling of superiority. But you'll survive that!

There is yet another problem that you might meet concerning piloting twin engine aeroplanes unless you are lucky enough to own or have a share in the twin you intend to fly. Some insurance companies are not at all happy about covering pilots with minimal multi engine experience and this can make it quite difficult to find a twin to hire, and thus ever manage to log the experience in twins that you need before you can hire one. Catch 22 for the newly fledged twin engine pilot. It can be an enormous help in this situation if you have a friend who is prepared (or who might be persuaded) to let you put in some P2 time in the right-hand seat of a multi engine aircraft until the hours totals in the multi engine columns of your logbook look more impressive than when you just finished your twin conversion. Once you have amassed around 25 to 30 hours of multi engine time it should prove easier to find suitable aircraft available for you to hire.

A twin engine aircraft appears at first to offer enhanced safety compared with a single, especially for night and over water flying but as already pointed out this can be somewhat illusory unless the pilot is right on top of his or her form and the circumstances (and aircraft) are favourable. Conversion to twins is the logical and necessary step up from single engine flying for all budding CPLs, but it actually offers fewer real benefits to the private flyer than might initially appear. And it doesn't come cheap. For the average private pilot, who doesn't have unlimited funds at his or her disposal, nor any serious aspirations in the direction of owning a twin, there are probably better ways of widening your flying experience before making the decision to master the gentle art of multi engine flying.

Loops, Rolls, Aresti and the Rest

The old adage about one person's meat being another person's poison is certainly very applicable to the gentle art of aerobatics. To some pilots the delight that can be obtained from pirouetting around the sky in a series of simple loops and rolls, or from performing choreography of complex aerobatic manoeuvres, is something that borders on the ecstatic. Many other pilots have a total aversion to the idea of throwing themselves about the heavens in an aeroplane; the very thought of positive and negative G-forces, of seeing the earth rotate around them and occasionally even appear somewhere down above their heads, fills them with revulsion.

I was introduced to aerobatics in rather an uncivilised way. On my very first flight as a student pilot, after about half an hour of a lesson termed 'air experience and the effects of controls' my over-exuberant RAF instructor suddenly said "Now you'd like to find out what a loop's like", and without any further ado he put the nose of the Miles Magister into what seemed to me a potentially lethal downward angle while my stomach rose into my gullet. Mother earth then vanished altogether, my guts lurched violently down, the landscape came into view again somewhere above my head and everything went very quiet for a moment before it seemed to me we were again suicidally diving straight down to meet the ground. "D'ya like that, eh?" I heard. I swallowed back a mouthful of bile and lied through my teeth, "Yes, it was great", whilst praying inwardly that he wouldn't treat me to any more nonsense like that.

A somewhat thoughtless demonstration like that has put many people off aerobatics for life. Fortunately for me however, other instructors later took the time to explain in advance what was involved in each manoeuvre, then demonstrated loops and rolls, followed me through on the controls and finally let me off solo to throw my aeroplane around the sky. I never achieved a level of aerobatic prowess that would have enabled me to take part in it as a competitive sport, but I did at least experience the thrills of coaxing Tiger Moths around slow rolls without falling out of the sky, and later enjoyed the extra performance of the Chipmunk which made all the standard manoeuvres seem that bit easier. Then I had the pleasure of taking Harvard's around sequences of aerobatics; that redoubtable machine may now look to today's generation of 21st century pilots like an ancient lumbering monster but it really is a delightfully agile aeroplane to fly. My most vivid memories of past aerobatic pleasures come however from the all too short spell I was lucky enough to spend as a jet fighter pilot. The Gloster Meteor F4's twin jet engines didn't give it the thrust to weight ratio of a Lightning (English-Electric variety I mean, this time), Panavia Tornado or Eurofighter Typhoon but for RAF pilots in the 1950s it marked a quantum step in performance, enabling us to twist the world around our aircraft in ways that had never before been possible.

Keeping Within Limits

As a civilian PPL flying for your own pleasure you will probably never be able to sample the joys of jet fighter aerobatics but that doesn't by any means imply that for you to take some aerobatic training would be a waste of either your time or effort. There is a great deal of fun to be had from even something as simple as a Cessna 152 Aerobat and, if the aerobatic aspect of aviation really begins to take your fancy, there are many other more agile aircraft than Cessna's easily available for PPL pilots to fly: old-timers like Stampes, Moths and Bückers; cheap to fly LAA types such as the Tipsy Nipper or the Hyperbipe; expense no object machines like warbirds and of course the specialist aerobatic aircraft like Zlins, CAPs, Extras and Pitts Specials. The Chipmunk, Beagle Pup and Slingsby T67 also are all excellent machines in which you can learn the basic manoeuvres. But you should never ever attempt to fly aerobatics in a standard aeroplane. Light aircraft aren't built like battleships. They are designed to meet certain certification standards and if you exceed their design load factor this can result in permanent structural damage, even if nothing obvious appears to have fallen asunder. Any overstrain of that nature can sometimes come to light only much later, when some unsuspecting pilot (possibly yourself) hits some severe turbulence for example, and experiences a structural failure all because some ass had tried to show off as a smart aerobatic pilot in a non-aerobatic aeroplane. Oh yes, I agree you probably have seen some pretty

Performing aerobatics can be a great way of improving your airmanship, enjoying yourself and entertaining spectators. But unfortunately, performed regularly overhead unappreciative resident's, aerobatics can also be a source of great annoyance.

impressive manoeuvres performed at air shows in seriously non-aerobatic aircraft, but these were being done by expert pilots who had learned the manoeuvres in structurally strong, aerobatic aircraft, and who were making absolutely sure that the stress limits on the standard machine were not being exceeded. Normal aerobatic loops, rolls and stall turns, properly executed, are well within the strength limitations of lots of standard aeroplanes; the problems are liable to come when some pilot makes a slight mistake and the manoeuvre doesn't go quite as intended. Then it is all too easy to put loads on airframes and engines that are far in excess of their normal design and certification limits. Being aware that such dangers exist, and knowing how to combat them, is all part of learning aerobatics. It is not a bad maxim to remember that if something starts to go wrong when you are part way through a manoeuvre, things are more probably going to get worse rather than better unless you do something positive about it, and pretty quickly too!

Quite apart from the sheer exhilaration involved in flying aerobatics (immensely important though that is to all enthusiastic aerobatic pilots) just learning how to perform them is also going to improve your overall flying ability. The coordination, the timing and judgement required, the self discipline needed to maintain safety at all times and the need for you to stay in reasonable physical shape yourself all help to produce a general sharpening up of your everyday airmanship and piloting skills.

Since spinning ceased to be a compulsory part of the PPL course in the UK many pilots have been let loose in the skies with no experience of anything other than relatively straight and level flight, with just the occasional steep turn and an odd stall and recovery. The very ladylike way that many training aircraft stall these days too, means that many of these pilots have no real experience of how an aeroplane responds and how it should be handled if it gets into an unusual attitude. There is no point in saying you are never going to get your aircraft into such a situation; you may end up having precious little choice in the matter. One day you may be flung around like a leaf in a storm by lee wave turbulence while flying over mountains, or perhaps you will have your aircraft picked up and tossed like a balsawood model aeroplane by the gust front associated with a thunderstorm. Even although the air traffic controller will always give you the mandatory full wake turbulence time interval on the approach after a heavy aircraft has landed, that is no absolute guarantee that an unseen wake vortex might not still be lurking by the runway to flick you half-over onto your back. If throughout your flying life you have never been in an aeroplane in an unusual attitude like that, you will be considerably less likely to know how to recover safely from it than would a pilot with some experience of aerobatics.

Getting Ready

Aerobatic experience is not something you should try to gain on your own; not initially at least. Many of the books about aerobatics do make some of the manoeuvres sound fairly straightforward, but there are traps for the unwary. Falling into some of these traps can wreak havoc with airframes and engines, not to mention pilots. No; your first venture into the world of aerobatics really must be in a suitable aircraft that's designed to perform aerobatics and in the company of an experienced aerobatic instructor. Until your instructor has gone through the basics with you and declared you fit to go and polish up your performance of loops, rolls and the rest on your own, please don't risk your aircraft and your neck by 'having a little go at it' by yourself.

There aren't any special requirements in the way of equipment or clothing laid down for aerobatic flying, but it is only sensible to be appropriately clad for the job. It is bad practice whilst aerobatting to hang on to the control column (or yoke) with a vice like grip but it is also essential that your hand doesn't slip off, so gloves that absorb perspiration are useful. They would also protect your hands from fire and injury should you be involved in an accident. Likewise a good set of flying overalls which fit closely at the neck, ankles and wrists will also give some fire protection. They'll help keep you warm in chilly weather and should ensure that your clothing doesn't snag controls. They will also give you useful zippered or Velcro sealed pockets in which you can keep items essential for the flight safely tucked away where they won't fall out and risk jamming the controls. Footwear should not be so heavy that it deadens your sensitivity to the rudder control but should also afford some measure of protection. Trainers give no real protection against fire or injury; reasonably light leather flying boots do. Many aerobatic aircraft have seats that are designed to take parachutes and, although there is no law or regulation saying you must wear a parachute to do aerobatics, it is good common sense to do so when possible. You are unlikely ever to need a 'chute but you should still make sure you know how to use one. Being stuck in an unrecoverable flat spin, or contending with a structural failure in the air, isn't exactly the best time or place to start working out the technique that is involved in abandoning that particular type of aircraft.

Aerobatics are full of esoteric names. It won't be long before you hear the term Aresti, which comes from the 'Aresti Cryptographic System', a type of shorthand that enables aerobatic manoeuvres to be drawn clearly and simply on paper. An Aresti dictionary contains about 30,000 different aerobatic manoeuvres but before you allow that awesome fact to dissuade you from even starting to learn any of them, take comfort in the knowledge that virtually every one of these is based on just four simple figures. These are the loop, the roll, the stall turn and the spin. How do you get from four to 30,000? Easy; an aeroplane has three planes of movement and if you consider how it is possible to combine and permutate the basic manoeuvres in each of these planes, and in all the intermediate angles that lie between them, you will begin to get the idea.

Types of Manoeuvre

The Inside Loop is probably the easiest manoeuvre for most pilots to perform well and it is also arguably the most spectacular basic manoeuvre for spectators to watch. It consists of a circle flown in the vertical plane with the pilot's head pointing towards the centre of the circle. (A loop was the first intentional aerobatic manoeuvre ever recorded; it was performed by a Russian, Peter Nesterov, on 20 August 1913 at Syretzk near Kiev and he was apparently clapped into the guardroom for 'needless audacity' as a reward for his efforts!) The Outside Loop, sometimes known as the 'Bunt', has the pilot's head directed towards the outside of the circle and is, in my personal opinion, one of the most pointless and uncomfortable things anyone ever invented to do with an aeroplane.

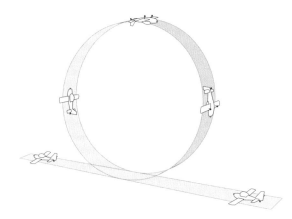

An inside loop is probably one of the easiest aerobatic manoeuvres to perform, but to fly it accurately requires skill too. It should take the form of a perfect circle with no 'dents' and tightening of the curve radius at the top should be avoided.

The Slow Roll involves using the ailerons to make the aircraft roll gently around its longitudinal axis, using the rudder and elevators to keep it as near straight and as level as possible. Halfway round you will find yourself hanging on your shoulder straps, so don't forget to pull them tight before you start. Tight straps are a prerequisite for the Stall Turn also. Here the aim is to get the aircraft climbing vertically and then to time your application of rudder exactly correctly, just as the aircraft is pointing vertically into the air and running out of puff towards the top of the climb but before it starts to tail slide back wards. Judge it right and you should achieve a 180° 'cartwheel' after which you have to ease the aircraft out of its subsequent vertical dive. Misjudge it and you can end up with a tail slide, a hammer-head stall,

A slow roll requires good co-ordination of the controls from the pilot and although perhaps not the most spectular aerobatic manoeuvre for spectators to watch, it is one of the most satisfying for the pilot to perform well.

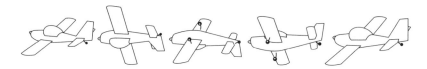

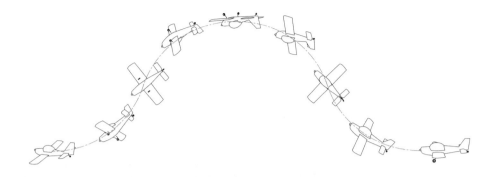

The barrel roll is a relatively easy manoeuvre to fly, with the aircraft following a sort of screw or coiled-spring path through the sky.

an upward skid and roll, or some other schemozzle. All aircraft have a favourite direction for stall turns. They tend to be easiest to perform to the right in aircraft fitted with British engines such as the Gipsy, Cirrus etc and are best done to the left in those powered by American Lycomings, Continentals etc. The aerobatic spin is not quite the same animal as the one that featured as a compulsory item in the PPL syllabus back in the good (or were they bad?) old days. Instead, it is a precision manoeuvre in which the pilot times both entry and recovery so as to ensure a predetermined number of turns and in such a way as to exit from the manoeuvre in exactly the desired direction. To achieve this the pilot has to practise until he or she knows the aircraft and its spin performance quite intimately. Perhaps it is just the difference between the pilot who is prepared to carry out a whole series of spins one after the other, just to get this right, and the pilot to whom more than one spin a month would be anathema, that marks the real difference between a born aerobatic enthusiast and the rest of the pilot population.

All complex aerobatic manoeuvres are combinations of the basic loop, roll, stall turn and spin. The rolling circle shown here looks simple but demands good coordination of control movements by the acrobatic pilot.

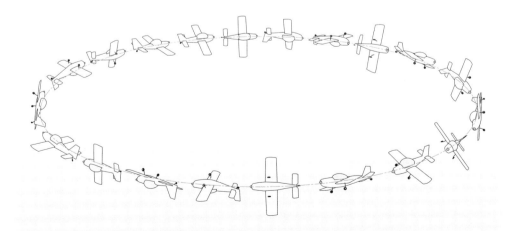

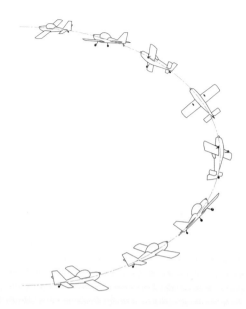

Beginners to aerobatic flying often find it difficult to realise that in rolling, whenever the wings approach the vertical, it is the elevators that are controlling direction, rather than the rudder.

All the other aerobatic manoeuvres and sequences are combinations and permutations of these basic four. Some have names with a history. The oldest perhaps is the 'Immelmann Turn'. It is so old that no one is really certain now what manoeuvre it was that Max Franz Immelmann actually flew. The popular belief is that his famous turn was a roll off the top of a loop, but it is doubtful if the Fokker Eindeckers he flew were capable of doing this. It seems more probable that the real Immelmann Turn was a steep climbing turn or what the Americans now term a 'Chandelle' although the truth about what an Immelmann really was is already lost in the mists of aviation antiquity. What is known as a 'Cuban Eight' (a double loop resembling a figure eight on its side) came into being when an American, Len Povey, who was at the time chief pilot for the Cuban revolutionary Fulgencio Batista, made a mess of a planned manoeuvre at a Miami air display and involuntarily performed this instead. After landing he was asked what that spectacular figure had been, so off the cuff he entitled it 'Cuban Eight'.

During my own days of piloting Gloster Meteors I managed once or twice to execute what was known then as a 'Zurakowski Turn' or 'Zurabatic Cartwheel'. Spectacular to view (and equally spectacular from the pilot's seat) this was named after Gloster's 1950s Polish test pilot Jan Zurakowski, who first performed it in public at Farnborough in 1951. You entered it as if to do a stall turn but when the vertical speed was almost zero and the aircraft was pointing vertically upwards, you chopped the power on one engine, leaving the other at full chat; the aircraft started to perform a normal stall turn but then went right through the vertically down position and up the other side again, to complete one and a half rotations in the yawing plane before finally entering a spin. So far as I am aware the Meteor was the only aircraft in which Zurabatic Cartwheels could be performed, although it is said that Zurakowski first managed it in a de Havilland Hornet. From the same era came the 'Porteous Loop' and the 'Derry Turn'. The former name commemorates the way Auster (and Beagle) chief test pilot Ranald Porteous did beautiful flick rolls from the top of a loop while flying an Auster Aiglet, also at Famborough. (Sadly for the memory of Ranald Porteous, his party trick has now been renamed the Avalanche.) The Derry Turn was a speciality of de Havilland test pilot John Derry and was a positive-g turn initiated by rolling through 270° in the opposite direction. Utterly spectacular, but requiring more rudder power and excess thrust than any PPL is ever likely to have at his or her disposal. Instead you can try your hand (given access to a sufficiently strong and powerful aircraft) at Torque Rolls, Inverted Spins, Hesitation Rolls, Flick Rolls, and Lomcevaks, which are really a whole family of manoeuvres derived from positive or negative flicks, torque reaction and gyroscopic precession. Most of these culminate in the aircraft tumbling end over end. Positively not for the novice, nor for the squeamish!

Competitive Sport

Competition aerobatics is a challenging field and one that attracts quite a few dedicated and highly skilled aerobatic pilots. It is recognised as an international sport under the Fédération Aéronautique Internationale and its regulations have been drawn up by the International Aerobatics Committee. There are regular aerobatic contests held, not only around the UK, but all over the world. These are pitched at varying levels of skill and ability, from club competitions through national contests and up to the International World Aerobatic Championships, which are currently held every two years. In the UK the Royal Aero Club has recognised the British Aerobatic Association (BAeA) as the representative body for the sport. Get involved in the British aerobatic scene and you will probably soon be visiting some of the British Aerobatic Association training camps to learn more of the arts and crafts involved. Then you will soon be able to start participating in competitions with names such as the Kernow, McLean, Don Henry, Roy Legg, McAully, Newbold, Tiger and Air Squadron Trophies. There is seldom a dull period of the year once you get caught up in this demanding and immensely satisfying sport.

Demonstration aerobatics at air shows and other events is something one can aspire to only after long hard hours of dedicated practice, and even then only if you have the aptitude and nerves for it. There is little point in performing a perfect sequence of manoeuvres five thousand feet above the heads of the crowd you are supposed to be entertaining. This is the one case when the otherwise sacrosanct rule about never aerobatting below 3,000 feet above the ground simply has to be ignored. Unfortunately, the statistics concerning the numbers of air show aerobatic pilots who have come to grief whilst performing, only serve to emphasise the importance of that 3,000 feet minimum rule for ordinary mortals. If, despite (or maybe even because of) these statistics, you still have an urge to get into aerobatics at air displays or other public events, you would have first to complete one important little formality. It is mandatory for all display pilots to have a Display Authorisation issued by the CAA. So if you have any serious leanings in that direction you had better get hold of CAP 403 on Flying Displays and Special Events and read it up in order to get all the necessary details.

You can fly aerobatics in many different types of aircraft that have been designed and stressed for it. The Champion Citabria shown here even has a name to match; Citabria is 'airbatic' written in a tail slide!

Just for Fun

Luckily however, aerobatics for one's own pleasure and satisfaction, as opposed to competition or display, are something else entirely. Aerobatic flying is something that can be thoroughly enjoyed by most competent pilots after a few hours of suitable training. It has often been said that to be a pilot and never to do aerobatics is rather like being married to a beautiful woman (or to a gorgeous man, presumably) and never to consummate the union. On the other hand (even though the earth is sometimes said to move during it) sexual intercourse seldom seems to cause feelings of vertigo, nausea, air-sickness and vomiting, whilst it has to be admitted that aerobatic flying quite frequently does this to a lot of pilots. If you happen to be one of these pilots, and if the impulse to throw up still persists after a few aerobatic lessons, then my advice would simply be to give up at that juncture. There is little point in making yourself miserable whilst trying to do something that should be bringing you pleasure. There are lots of other things you can do with aeroplanes and some of these are bound to suit your particular constitution much better than aerobatics. Swallowing pills or potions is not always a good idea either. Most air-sickness remedies and medicines have the effect of slowing down your reactions and making you sleepy, neither of which side effects is conducive to performing well as a pilot, aerobatic or otherwise.

Safety Factors

Aerobatic instruction should always start with a revision of stalling and an introduction (if you have never done it before) to spinning and recovery. These are necessary since both form part of aerobatics, often intentionally but occasionally involuntarily, should you happen to make a bit of a mess of a manoeuvre. Then comes recovery from unusual attitudes; you never know when you might find yourself in one of these. Basic instruction in the fundamentals of aerobatics should take somewhere around five or six hours for the average PPL pilot before the instructor is likely to feel ready to let you off on your own to 'slip the surly bonds of Earth and dance the skies on laughter-silvered wings' to use John Magee's words from his poem High Flight. Then it is just a matter of practice and, if you want to fly to aerobatic competition or display standard, still more practice.

Aerobatic flying involves stressing yourself and your aeroplane to a much higher degree than most other forms of flying. This is why you should never be tempted to do aerobatics in an aircraft that is not specifically designed and cleared for the job. It is also why you must be prepared to admit freely if you have done anything in the air that might have overstrained the aircraft or its engine. It is all too easy to pull more g than you intended or to let the engine rpm build up beyond the red line. If you do, and you fail to have the machine carefully inspected afterwards, you could be responsible for a mechanical failure on a subsequent flight; perhaps your own, perhaps someone else's.

Performing aerobatics involves more risk than conventional right way up flying; that much has to be accepted. But the amount of extra risk can be kept within acceptable limits by observing sensible rules. Pre-flight inspections must be more thorough, including checking that no loose objects are on board; securing all harness straps where they cannot interfere with controls and double checking harness tightness and buckle locking. HASELL checks are essential before each set of manoeuvres, and the H for height is perhaps the most vital of these; no less than 5,000 feet agl when you start and always stop your aerobatics while you are still no lower than 3,000 feet agl. Once a satisfactory aerobatic session is over and you are heading back towards the airfield again, you might quite well find yourself in a slightly euphoric state. You have to make a decided effort then to calm down and try not to behave like those crazy car drivers you can often see on their way home from watching a Grand Prix. Remember you are back in the real world once again, so exercise some restraint and revert to normal airmanship standards as you approach the airfield circuit. Nobody there is really going to appreciate a semi-aerobatic rejoin procedure.

For safety's sake make sure you get a good checkout in the aeroplane involved so you can enjoy your aerobatics without overstraining your aircraft; restrain any impulse you may feel to do aerobatics at low level; exercise your art away from built up areas and busy airspace and constantly maintain a specially good look out for other aircraft. Your aerobatics should then be pretty safe, as well as being excellent fun. The remainder of your day to day flying in all its aspects should benefit from increased safety too; for there is no other form of flying I know that does quite so much as aerobatics to hone a pilot's skills and to enhance his or her airmanship and self confidence.

Formation Flying

There is no real reason for me to place this section about Formation Flying immediately after the section about Aerobatics, except that the two seem to be closely associated with each other in the minds of many pilots. This is most probably due to the fact that the quintessence of formation flying often involves those magnificent formation aerobatic displays performed by the Red Arrows, Fricke Tricolored and Patrouille de France military teams, and by the Rothmans, Toyota and other (generally company sponsored) civilian formation teams which perform at many air shows. This type of spectacular formation flying is certainly beyond the capabilities of most private pilots; the many hours of flying that are involved in perfecting the performance of a team like the Red Arrows would cost far more than most civilian pilots could ever afford. Yet there is no reason at all why you should not learn at least some of the basics of formation flying.

Best known experts in the gentle art of formation flying are undoubtedly the various military teams including the Red Arrows of the Royal Air Force, the Patrouille de France and Italy's Frecce Tricolore, shown here in an impeccable formation of their Aeromacchi MB 339 aircraft.

What use is formation flying? Like aerobatics, its practical uses in civil flying are limited but it does help tremendously to develop your general handling skills, reactions and powers of anticipation. It can occasionally also be of practical value. Being able to follow a shepherd aircraft if you ever were to become lost, possibly above cloud, is one example of where the ability to formate safely could be very useful. Another would be if your airspeed indicator failed for any reason; it could then be an enormous help in maintaining accurate approach and landing speeds if you were able to formate on another aircraft of similar performance; better by far than stalling as you tried to turn finals. If you are ever called upon to assist in checking the operation of another aircraft's undercarriage it is a great help when you are confident about flying in formation with it. Sometimes it can also be handy to be able to fly a non-radio aircraft in formation with a radio equipped one in order to let it use the other's radio calls to gain entry to restricted airspace. Air to air photography can be a hazardous business if the pilots involved have no experience of formation flying, but it becomes much easier if the pilot of at least one of the aircraft is skilled in the art of keeping station.

For certain species of birds, of course, formation flying has been part of their airborne repertoire since time immemorial. Geese, ducks and swans are well known exponents of the art but no ornithologist seems to be absolutely certain why they do it. Theories abound, concerning self-protection, migratory navigation and the possibility that weaker or more fatigued birds at the rear gain some extra lift from vortices left behind by the leaders. For military pilots too, formation flying has long been a basic part of flying. WWI pilots of the Royal Flying Corps (and their French and German counterparts) soon learned to keep one another company in the air to generate additional fire-power, to have extra pairs of eyes watching for the enemy and to give each other mutual support. No-one who saw them will ever forget the sight and the sound of the vast formations of US bombers and their escort fighters in WW2, as they formed up over England and resolutely flew in unbroken formation across enemy territory towards their targets. The majority of the world's military pilots are still trained to fly in close formation and are kept in regular practice at it.

Fig. 15 " Ready for Take-Off "

Fig. 16 " Opening Throttle "—
" Closing Throttle "

Fig. 17 " Lower Undercarriage "—
" Raise Undercarriage "

Fig. 18 " Lower Flaps "—" Raise Flaps "

If you fancy the idea of flying in close proximity to another aeroplane then you must learn how to do it properly. Just like aerobatics, formation flying is not something you should try to teach yourself. Get hold of an instructor to show you how. That might be something of a problem in itself, for it is not by any means every instructor who is able to fly formation, never mind teach others how to do it. In UK flying circles, if you look for an instructor who occasionally is seen wearing an RAF or RN tie then you might strike lucky. But for safety's sake resist any temptation to have a go at formation flying without being taught the basics first. I have seen ad hoc attempts at formation flying made by private pilots to impress friends on the ground. Believe me, they wouldn't impress anyone. And I have also lost a good friend as a result of an attempted formation air to air photographic session where a misunderstanding brought one of the aircraft to grief, killing all on board. It takes quite a lot of skill and practice to fly safely in close proximity to other aircraft and to follow your formation leader. The exercise is particularly demanding if the air is at all turbulent or if the aircraft are not of similar types or at least types that have similar performance.

A system of hand signals developed in the days of open cockpit service aircraft was still being taught in the Royal Air Force to pilots of the early jet fighters. The same signals are still used when formation flying in open-cockpit civil aircraft today.

Formation Protocol

Conventionally, aircraft in a formation are numbered; the leader is always number 1 and when flying in a symmetrical formation those aircraft to the leader's left usually have odd numbers and those to the right, even. (This system is the RAF one; if your instructor happens to have been taught formation flying in the Fleet Air Arm then you may well be taught the RN system which is, of course, different.) There are several standard formations and dozens of elaborate ones such as the well known 'Concorde' and others flown by the Red Arrows etc. The simplest is probably the Vic formation, where each of the following aircraft tries to station themselves in a Vee shape, their wingtips level with the tail plane of the aircraft ahead and about half a span out from the wingtip. In Line Abreast, the wing aircraft move forward to align their wingtips with the leader's wingtips. Echelon Port is like Vic but with all aircraft to the leader's left and stepped towards the rear. Echelon Starboard is the other way round (these are also now known as Echelon Left and Echelon Right). In Line Astern the leader is straight ahead of, but above, the next aircraft and any subsequent aircraft are similarly stepped down so that they avoid flying in the slipstream of preceding machines. The last of the standard formations needs at least four aircraft and is the Box, which is a simple Vic with number 4 stepped down and directly behind the leader, wingtips aligned with the tail plane of numbers 2 and 3. It is useful to spend some time on the ground looking carefully at the aircraft you are going to be flying alongside, picking out how you are going to align yourself with it, getting familiar with what its perspective looks like when your wingtip is roughly half a span off its wingtip.

There are other conventions you might have to learn too, such as conventional signs that are always used by the leader in open cockpit aircraft (and often in closed cockpit aircraft too) to indicate the next intended manoeuvres and conventional radio calls that are used for the

Formation flying is by no means restricted to military aircraft but should not be attempted by a PPL holder without some instruction in the air by a pilot who knows how to do it safely. Here three Cub pilots show how neatly they have learned to fly their machines.

same purpose. These calls take the form of 'Manoeuvre, manoeuvre, GO!' with GO being the signal to start the 'Turning right' or 'Smoke on' or whatever. A thorough briefing before flight is essential so that all pilots involved know in advance what is the aim of the trip, what action is proposed in the event of bad weather, where the formation will meet to join up (always an 'interesting' stage that, for the newcomer to formation flying) and what changes of formation are anticipated during the flight. In the initial stages, formation take-off and landing is a strict no-no, and even for experienced pilots, ATC agreement for this must be obtained in advance. The easiest way of joining formation is usually to approach the leader from behind and below, adjusting power as you gradually slip into the desired position; this avoids rushing along level at full throttle to catch up and then finding yourself unable to slow down soon enough to avoid overtaking number 1. That can be distinctly dangerous if you lose sight of the lead ship behind you, as well as being more than slightly embarrassing.

Once you have mastered station keeping while straight and level, gentle climbs and descents should present you with no great problems. Turning comes next; gentle ones only, 15° bank angle at most to start with. The aircraft on the outside of a turn have farther to fly than the lead ship, so need a bit of extra throttle to keep up. Conversely the inside aircraft have to slow down a bit. Changing from one formation to another looks childishly simple when you see the expert formation teams doing it. When you try it yourself you will soon find that it is quite an art form and one that you need to rehearse on the ground before you ever attempt it in the air. The trick of course is to make absolutely certain that no two aeroplanes ever try to occupy the same bit of the sky at the same time in the course of the change.

Being close to other aircraft in the air is something you normally avoid, for obvious safety reasons. When you deliberately set out to keep close company with other aircraft you are, of course, making your flying that little bit more hazardous, but the extra risk is not great provided you all stick to the rules. Never attempt any DIY impromptu formation; that is simply asking for trouble. Always prepare thoroughly for the trip and ensure that all the pilots concerned really do know what is going to be performed. All you have to do is treat formation flying with the respect it deserves and you will find it will become yet another exciting and satisfying facet of your flying.

Splashdown

Seaplane flying is something which most British pilots associate in their minds more with Canada, New Zealand or Florida perhaps, than with the UK. Yet the opportunity exists at more than one location in the UK, to learn how to fly from water. This can be an interesting experience and one that is decidedly different from the way the vast majority of flyers get their aeroplanes into the air and back down again. It must be admitted that a seaplane rating is of but limited practical use in Britain. Despite that, though, there are quite a few amphibians and seaplanes on the British register and some of these are available for hire. Although several enthusiastic individuals have tried to expand the opportunities for water-based flying in this country, suitable facilities still remain few and far between. There are certain legal complications, associated with the law of trespass, which can adversely affect the operation of aircraft from water in England, but in Scotland the law of trespass is entirely different (virtually non-existent in point of fact) and it is in theory permissible to operate a seaplane from almost any loch or other body of water in Scotland although some local; and National Park authorities do make efforts to restrict these activities. Britain's busiest water flying centre, Caledonian Seaplanes, which offers you the opportunity of adding a seaplane rating to your PPL in magnificent surroundings, is located on Lochearn in Perthshire.

Alternatively, float plane instruction is available in various other places in the world including (close to both Disney World and Orlando in Florida) Jack Brown's Seaplane Base in Winter Haven. This centre claims to have trained more seaplane pilots than any other facility in the world. It is a long way to travel if the seaplane rating is all you are after and the relatively small difference in aircraft hourly hire rates between the Scottish and the American establishments will scarcely cover the travel costs involved. The seaplane rating should involve an average PPL pilot in little more than five hours of flying and can easily be completed within a couple of

Swans and cygnets at the Lochearn water aerodrome seem to be on perfectly friendly terms with pilots and Pipers with floats. This is an excellent training facility at which to qualify in the UK for your PPL seaplane rating.

days. The UK rating also involves passing a 20 question multiple-choice exam paper on seamanship set by the CAA, who also publishes a guide to studying for the seamanship examination. Another useful bible for the would-be water flyer is How to Fly Floats published by Edo Corporation, the well known American manufacturer of seaplane floats. You should really read both these publications, and be sure you have thoroughly digested their contents, before you start the airborne and waterborne parts of the seaplane rating course.

    The airborne part is really quite insignificant. If you can fly a land plane, particularly if you have some experience of tail wheel aircraft, then you can fly a float plane. The weight of the floats reduces climb performance a little compared to a similar wheeled machine and you need to apply rather bigger boot fulls of rudder to compensate for the machine's altered directional stability. The aircraft also stalls at a slightly higher speed and when the throttle is closed (or if the engine fails on take-off) the drag of the floats makes the nose drop quite sharply, the airspeed falls rapidly away and the glide approach is appreciably steeper than normal. But it is essentially the business of handling the float plane on the surface of water that you have to learn; that and getting the beast off the water and back on to it again. A bit of experience in dinghy sailing helps here, to give you some idea of how you should handle the movement of the aircraft on the water, counteract wind effect and steer to where you intend to start the take-off run. With wide expanses of water normally available, take-off and landing can usually be into wind, so crosswind effects can be forgotten. There are lots of strange new terms for you to learn too. You will find out how to 'sail' (or 'idle taxi') the aircraft slowly, 'displace' (or 'taxi') it slightly faster, 'plough' (or in America 'plow') it fast enough to lift the front of the floats up clear of the water, or 'step taxi' it, when the floats are skimming the surface at perhaps 30 knots or so. The next stage after step taxiing is the actual take-off and on a low power training float plane it sometimes seems to take an eternity to reach this stage. If the water is glassy smooth your little floatplane may in fact never reach unstick speed at all, unless you use one of the tricks of the marine flyer's trade.

From Airborne to Waterborne

Water landings, nearly always being into wind, present few problems, unless the water happens to be glassy smooth. It can then be infernally difficult to judge your height above the surface. Bear in mind that the floats are rigidly attached to the aircraft with no oleos or bungees or leaf spring undercarriage legs to help absorb any jolts. It is obvious that hefty impacts with the water surface are to be avoided; otherwise damage to the airframe is quite liable to occur. To achieve a gentle touchdown in smooth water conditions, you sometimes have to make a low pass and chuck out something that floats to give you a clue as to where the surface level is as you make your next approach to touch down. Otherwise you can try to touch down close to something like a buoy, a shrub on the water's edge or a moored boat, which has the same effect. Or you just have to descend very gradually, holding the airspeed just a knot or five above the stall, and wait patiently for the float keels to score the surface. At that juncture you close the throttle and hold the stick back and you should be safely down. My most vivid memory of my own limited experience of water flying is of watching the opposite shore of the loch as it seemed to be approaching me with undesirable rapidity and my becoming supremely conscious of the fact that manufacturers always seem to forget to fit seaplanes with any brakes! Fortunately, once a seaplane decelerates a little with the stick held well back, it comes 'off the step' and slows up surprisingly smartly. That is the time you stop being an aircraft pilot and find you back as a sailor in charge of the equivalent of an aerial catamaran.

Getting your seaplane rating is one thing, using it is another. Opportunities for that are somewhat limited in Britain and you may be pushed even to keep it valid. For this you require at least twelve hours of flight time (at least six of these as PIC) in a single engine land or seaplane, plus twelve take-offs from water and twelve landings on water during the twelve months preceding the expiry of your seaplane rating. None the less a seaplane rating isn't something that many people acquire and it is definitely a nice piece of one up man ship to have, another feather in your flyer's cap. As something to talk about around the flying club bar of an evening it will cap your club mates' boasts about IMC ratings any day. It is not expensive, as flying accomplishments go, and it lets you extend your piloting experience in yet another interesting and stimulating direction.

Rallies, Fly-ins and Other Fun Events

There is no need for you to become a member of anything other than the world of private flying before you can take part in and enjoy many of the dozens of open events organised every year by enthusiasts all over the country, and indeed all over the world. I am thinking about all those happenings that go under the various names of Fly-In, Air Rally, Breakfast Patrol, Wings and Wheels, Easter Air Weekend, Old Timer Meeting and so on. Thumb through your favourite flying magazine and see what is on offer and which of the events you feel might be of most interest to you. Once you have made the slight initial effort of phoning the organisers to put your name down for the fly-in (or whatever they call it) you should soon find yourself beginning to get sucked into the mainstream of things. You do a bit of flight planning to get to wherever the get together is taking place and then, when the great day arrives and you have actually flown in, you will perhaps start to wonder why on earth you bothered to go there at all. Everyone there, apart from yourself, will seem to know everyone else and you will quite probably, at the beginning, feel somewhat left out of things. But flying enthusiasts being what they are, you can be pretty sure that it will not be long before you are every bit as caught up in things as all the old hands. You are highly unlikely to reach the end of the event without making solemn promises to be back again next year, or to meet some of the others at another happening which is due to take place in the interim. Many of these events involve some degree of usually fairly light hearted competition. Hardy annual events of this type which are popular with British pilots include the International Air Rallies of Jersey, Guernsey and Malta. It is quite possible to attend and enjoy these without bothering to participate in their competitive aspects if these tend to be at all off putting from your point of view. Then there are the many fly-ins, under various names and guises, which are essentially social in nature but sometimes do have a little of the competitive element included, just to spice them up a bit. Again these competitive bits are always voluntary. You won't be pressured into making spot landings, or dropping flour bags, or flying in aerial treasure hunts, if you would rather just quietly enjoy the sunshine and the company. Having attended many of these gatherings, I'll be surprised if you don't soon find yourself itching to have a go at some of the less serious of these little aeronautical challenges. They all add to the fun of what generally turns out to be a thoroughly enjoyable day or weekend out.

Here a group of owners and pilots of Grumman aircraft from all around Europe are getting together in May 2004 for their annual European meeting.

This club fly-out to a neighbouring sky dive aerodrome involved an interesting mix of microlights and conventional single engine aircraft.

Set Your Own World Record

Mention world records to most PPL pilots and they will immediately think of pioneering pilots like Bert Hinckler, Amy Johnson and Charles Lindbergh, or more modern aviation achievers such as Dick Rutan and Jeana Yeager flying un-refuelled and non-stop around the world in their Voyager aircraft. Alternatively your minds will turn immediately to powerful jet aircraft like the Lockheed Blackbird which has hurtled from London to New York at an average speed of just under 1250 knots (2,320 kilometres per hour, to be precise). Then there is the altitude record for winged aircraft which is now well above 350,000 feet (106,680 m). There seems to be precious little chance surely, of any pilot of a typical light aircraft having a crack at setting a world record.

But, surprisingly enough, there is. If you are interested, and have at least 100 hours P1 time in your logbook, there is no reason at all why you shouldn't make an attempt to have your name added to the list of illustrious world record holders which is kept by the Fédération Aéronautique Internationale (FAI) in Paris. There isn't even any need for you to go to the trouble of contacting the FAI. They have a representative in the UK in the form of the Royal Aero Club and it is the RAeC's Records, Racing and Rally Association, which looks after all record attempts by British registered fixed wing powered aircraft, and by all UK pilots. There is no need either, strangely enough, to fly a particularly fast, powerful or long-range aircraft in order to be able to set a world record. Still interested? Or simply puzzled, the way most pilots are when they first find out about this record breaking business?

You don't need to have access to an exotic aeroplane like Rutan's famous round the world aircraft Voyager before you can make or break a world record. You can do it in something as simple as a Tomahawk, a Taylorcraft or a Tipsy Nipper.

There are literally thousands of records within the flying scene that have either never yet been set, or have already been made and are therefore already on the FAI's record books just waiting for someone else to come along and break them. In many cases that someone else could easily be a 101 hour PPL pilot flying a perfectly standard training or touring light aircraft. The business of setting and breaking records need not even be a very expensive exercise for you, provided you are sensible and choosy about the record or records you want to set or break. The easiest to tackle are the speed records from one point to another. Endurance records and distance records are a bit trickier for normal light aircraft to establish these days and altitude records involve some special equipment, including a barograph. If you were silly enough to try something obvious for your speed record, like London to Paris, you will immediately run into problems for lots of expensive hardware has already pushed that one (and many others like it) well out of reach of the private pilot in a standard Cessna trainer. There is, though, no need for record attempts to be made between major or obvious city pairs. You might well find that Cambridge to Cork, Norwich to Namur, or perhaps Plymouth to Poitiers, are routes all waiting for records to be set in your class of aircraft. Yes, even if someone has already chalked up their name on the record for a particular route while flying one type of aircraft, that doesn't mean you cannot set up a record of your own for the same route while flying a larger or smaller aircraft. There are categories for land planes, seaplanes and amphibians and different divisions for piston engines, turboprops, jet engines and even rocket powered aircraft. The piston engine land plane category is further subdivided into six weight defined classes, with take-off weights under 300kg, 500kg, 1,000kg, 1,750kg, 3,000kg and 6,000kg. As you can imagine this gives plenty of scope for all sorts of aircraft to set all sorts of speed records.

To go about setting a record (and incidentally, if successful, acquiring a handsome Record Certificate to frame and hang on the office or living room wall) you must first get a Royal Aero Club Competitor's Licence, (for detail see the website http://airraceuk.com/main/frameset.htm) You apply for this to the RAeC, Records, Racing and Rally Association (usually known as the 3 Rs). Once you have this (and be warned, the application form asks you to find someone willing to sign certifying that he or she confirms you are sane!) you are free to decide which world record to attempt. The RAeC 3 Rs will check for you whether any route you propose is available for a new record, or if you have an existing record to beat. Perhaps the next holiday trip you are planning (or your next business flight to see a customer or visit an exhibition) might be an opportunity for you to set or break a world air speed record as well?

There is another fee to pay before you go, in order to register the attempt in advance with the Royal Aero Club but from there on the formalities are few. The RAeC doesn't tie you down too closely so far as the time or the date of the attempt are concerned, knowing that weather is an important factor. Nor is it necessary for you to have RAeC observers to check you out at take-off and in at your destination. The times of take-off and landing, as recorded by Air Traffic Control at a controlled airfield, are readily accepted. If the attempt is between points other than controlled airfields, then it gets a little trickier, but the RAeC might even go so far as to have an official observer fly with you in the aircraft to confirm timings.

Some private pilots have become quite hooked on setting world records. Most others are quite content to have just one or two of the record certificates to impress their friends and colleagues. Record setting is certainly not a complicated pastime, nor is it necessarily expensive. Sometimes it might even be possible to find commercial sponsorship for a world record attempt if you use your imagination in picking the record and go about things the correct way, making use of any contacts you have. Record breaking sounds quite an exciting affair, yet it doesn't add any extra risk or danger to the flying involved and the aircraft insurance policy will normally cover an attempt of the type outlined here without any extra premium. Adding a record attempt to almost any international flight can give the trip an interesting bit of extra kick. (Records can be set within one country too, but there is a minimum distance then of at least 400km, which is approximately 216nm.) Selecting, planning and carrying out an occasional world air record attempt can be great fun and gives any PPL yet another good reason to use his or her licence in yet another imaginative way.

The Dawn to Dusk

This is a British event in which you might like to consider participating, and which again doesn't require you to become a member of any special organisation. The Dawn to Dusk International Flying Competition is an annual contest in which private pilots are invited to stretch their imaginations and broaden their flying experience. Sponsored by Pooley's (of Flight Guide fame) this is an original and unusual sort of competition in which you, the entrant, can write most of the rules yourself. You decide what sort of flying you might like to do and to what purpose, then make your own plans, set your own time (within fairly broad limits) and off you go and do it. Despite the name (which isn't really taken too literally) it is certainly not necessary for you to stay in the air from first light until sunset. There is, however, an airborne minimum time of eight hours to be observed (or seven if you have logged under 100 hours as P1). You are at liberty to spend your Dawn to Dusk day doing something you have dreamed up all by yourself, based on your own interests and initiative. You may consider your flight to be educational, historical, geographical or inspirational, or you may decide to fly some other mission of the 'just because it is there' sort. The main requirement is that whatever you

There is no need for a sophisticated aeroplane in order to enter the Dawn to Dusk. It is even advantageous to fly something fairly basic like this Cessna 170 because for any given task, the markers award more points to pilots flying simpler aeroplanes to allow for the extra effort involved.

endeavour to do it must have a fair degree of originality to it. Having flown your competition flight, all that remains for you to do is to write up your log and flight description and send these off, together with all your maps and charts, landing and fuel receipts etc. These make up your entry. Then you just have to await the judges verdict on what you have submitted to them.

The Dawn to Dusk International Flying Competition can be flown by any pilot, using any type of aircraft from a microlight upwards. The simpler the aircraft, the more marks are awarded for any particular task, to take into consideration the extra effort involved. Low hour's pilots also score more marks for similar tasks than more experienced contenders. The marking is rather a complicated matter but in the end the winner receives the premier award of the Duke of Edinburgh Trophy. According to the Duke of Edinburgh himself (who has for many years taken a keen interest in the Competition) he suspects that the marking is there just to give the judges something to do; the real satisfaction comes from taking part. The Dawn to Dusk certainly has inspired some interesting and challenging flying in the past and often proves to be the ideal catalyst to get some private pilots out of their comfortable, but boring, ruts to discover for themselves just how much more challenge and satisfaction the flying of small aeroplanes has to offer.

Air Racing

During the interwar years air races were one of the mainstays of light aviation. Enthusiastic pilots, professional and amateur alike, turned up to race each other in such events as the King's Cup Air Race, which was first held in 1922 over a course from Croydon to Glasgow and back. The Schneider Trophy dates back even earlier, to its debut in Monaco in 1913. The Grosvenor Challenge Cup was for aircraft of 150hp or less. There have been many 'one off' air races like the MacRobertson Race of 1934 from England to Australia or the Daily Mail's Transatlantic Race of 1969. Now, however, these spectacles seem to have lost a great deal of their appeal to the public and air races tend to be the preserve of a limited number of keen pilots, enthusiasts and specialists. You can still enter for and fly a Schneider Trophy race, but it bears little resemblance to the enormously prestigious events of that name that were held in the 1930s. On the other hand, the average PPL pilot had no chance of participating in these, whilst the current Schneider Trophy Races most definitely are open to all, as long as they

Air racing can involve many different types of aircraft, specially designed machines like the Cassutt racer shown here, warbirds (as seen earlier) and also standard production aircraft that participate in the current Schneider Trophy series and other air races.

qualify. Other events of this nature which make up the air racing calendar in the British Isles include the City Livery Trophy, Bill Entress Trophy, Battle of Britain Trophy, Claddagh Trophy, Grosvenor Trophy, Stewards Cup and the King's Cup Races. So if you develop a taste for air racing and want to compete against the best, there are plenty of events to choose from at venues all around the UK and Ireland. There is a racing pilots' championship, and points towards winning this can be earned by securing a place in each of the qualifying events.

Most of these races are based on the handicap system and so to some extent you are racing the handicapper as much as the other competitors. The handicaps are calculated on the known performance of the aircraft involved, and the handicapper's aim is to have each aircraft take-off at a given time dependent on these calculations, so that theoretically all should arrive simultaneously at the finish. The fact that they don't is due to how well the aeroplanes have been tweaked to squeeze extra performance out of them, to the flying skills of the pilots and to a certain measure of good or bad luck. You can enter most of these races in almost any type of aircraft: home builds, old timers, production Piper's and Cessna's etc, and occasionally you even find the odd piston engine or jet fighter aircraft entered. The air racing scene is no place for owners or pilots who dislike the idea of their aero engines being belted at full throttle virtually throughout each race, nor for you if you are uncomfortable with the idea of hurtling round pylons or markers at low level and overtaking slower aircraft which loom up in front of you during the race. Overtaking is easier than on a Formula 1 Grand Prix motor racing circuit, but it can still have its exciting moments.

Excitement Unlimited

For real excitement, especially from the spectator point of view, what is known as Unlimited Class air racing is hard to beat. The home for this is in America, more specifically at Reno in Nevada, where each September the National Air Races are held. The aircraft are nearly all World War II piston engine fighters, which scream along at low level over the dessert; throttles wide open, racing at up to 400mph around circuits marked by tall pylons at each corner. There are also many other races in America for all sorts of aircraft types. What they call the T-6 Races are restricted to what we know in Britain as the North American Harvard two-seat trainer. Then there are Formula One races for small, fixed undercarriage aircraft with limited engine displacement; these are also raced occasionally in Britain, with Duxford a popular venue for the European Formula One Championships.

Like aerobatics, air racing is not every pilot's cup of tea but it does tend to become a real fascination for many pilots who decide to give it a try. Competing in the typical races run in the British Isles you will find is not an over expensive activity for an enthusiastic pilot to pursue. Unless your pockets are very deep and well lined I would strongly advise you to steer clear of Unlimited Class racing though. That is horrendously expensive stuff. Even as a spectator on the ground, watching the gaggle of different types of aircraft inexorably catching up with each other as they approach the finish of a handicap air race, can make a thrilling spectacle. Imagine what it could do for your blood pressure if you were actually up there piloting one of the average speed aircraft, trying all the tricks you knew in order to overhaul the slower types ahead of you and wondering all the while whether there was some faster machine breathing down your neck and liable to pip you at the post. If that sort of idea gets your adrenalin pumping and your pulse racing, maybe you should think about getting your aeroplane racing too.

Precision Flying

Do you enjoy meticulous airmanship, skilful piloting and really accurate navigation? If your answer is yes, then you might be interested in the British Precision Pilots' Association. They organise competitions and events several times a year and these quite often include a beginners' introductory event, where you can find out more details of what precision flying is all about before you commit yourself in any way. After your introduction you are permitted one full competitive event as an outsider and then, if you wish to continue with the sport, you must join the Association. You can't really ask for a much fairer way than that of introducing you gently to the sport. Although it is still very much a minority sport among British pilots, precision flying is very popular in other parts of the world, notably Eastern Europe and South America, and there are regular international competitions which culminate in the biannual World Championships.

Precision Flying has long been a very important part of the training of military and naval pilots but the idea of civilian precision flying competitions appears to have originated during the late 1940s in Sweden. The early contests that were held in Sweden were designed simply as fun ways of encouraging private pilots to polish up the basic skills they had learned during their PPL course. Basic among these skills was visual navigation, with the emphasis on the chart and compass, stopwatch and the famous mark one eyeball. These skills are still the key elements of most precision flying competitions. Entrants are expected to do different things at different competitions (it would after all soon become a bit boring otherwise) and to some extent the navigation exercises can be said to resemble orienteering routes or car club rally and treasure hunt events. The organisers pit their wits against the competitors, who in turn put their skills to work against each other. A typical competition could perhaps involve you being given somewhat cryptic route instructions, from which you have to prepare a flight plan within a given time limit and without the aid of any electronic whizz-sticks, Psion organisers etc. You then have to fly the route you have worked out and carry out a series of exercises during the flight. These could include pinpointing photographs of ground features near the track (and perhaps being sharp enough to identify some photos you've been given that are of things that resemble, but aren't really the ones you are actually flying over). Or you could have to mark your charts to indicate precisely where conspicuous 'targets' have been laid out, or describe what colour or shape these targets are. To make life more interesting you are also being timed by ground observers at turning points and elsewhere, and you are expected to pass each checkpoint within a very narrow margin (plus or minus a couple of seconds or so) of the ETAs calculated from the aircraft's declared airspeed. Fastest aircraft generally are flagged off first, slowest last, to prevent bunching or overtaking en route.

At the end of this navex there is often something along the lines of a spot landing contest, but this is generally rather more sophisticated than your average club affair. You could be asked to make one landing in a normal configuration with power and flaps as required, then a flapless glide approach to land or (if the organisers were feeling particularly evil-minded that day) maybe a glide approach that has to clear a two-metre high obstruction just 50 metres from the touchdown marker line. You don't just lose points for over or undershooting the line; they mark you down for landing nose wheel first or together with the mains, for bouncing, touching one main wheel before the other, etc. After all, it is called precision flying! At some of the bigger competitions, instead of having eagle eyed watchers to determine where your touchdown actually happens, the runway has a special carpet spread over it at the critical area. Pressure cells embedded in this mat are then used to give a technologically accurate definition of your precise landing point. It is very difficult to argue about these results afterwards.

No Need for Special Gear

One great advantage that this sport has is that you do not need to kit up with lots of expensive special equipment or even a special aeroplane. Slow aircraft have certain advantages over fast ships; the better ground visibility from high wing machines gives them a slight advantage over their low wing brethren. Polish precision pilots love the Wilga with its superb visibility, lots of cockpit glazing, high wing and excellent slow speed performance. But plenty of British pilots swear by bog standard Cessna 152s or 172s and the like. Some real fanatics have fitted their aircraft with little extra downward looking windows that can help then spot ground landmarks and targets. Some like to remove the right hand front seat to give the pilot more elbow room and the rear seat navigator more space for his or her clobber. And that inexpensive clobber, charts, maps, stopwatches, marker pens, pencils, erasers and clipboard, really comprise the only accoutrements you need before you can participate.

Essentials for Success

Precision flying always requires very thorough pre-flight preparation, really accurate piloting and navigation skills, and sharp eyes. Frequently you need a twisted (crossword puzzler's) mind to work out some of the cryptic clues and invariably you and your navigator must have the patience and ability to forgive each other after landing, for all the 'stupid so-and-so' epithets you probably used during the competition. It is all very similar to a good hectic car rally in fact. It can be great fun and local (as opposed to international) events are usually pretty informal, although even at these you will find most of the entrants take the whole thing reasonably seriously. Have a go at a precision flying competition sometime. It is likely to mean that next time you are heading off to navigate yourself from A to B, you will probably do it a great deal more accurately. And, as another bonus, you could well find yourself making a far better landing than usual when you reach B too.

Join the Club

This chapter does not contain by any means a complete listing of all the specialist activities that are ready and waiting to welcome any private pilot who wants to come in and join the fun. As well as the various well known flying clubs and schools, flying groups and aircraft partnerships, there are dozens of other organisations and associations that can help broaden a private pilot's interests and enhance his or her overall enjoyment of flying.

World's Biggest Pilots' Club

The Aircraft Owners and Pilots Association of the UK (AOPA UK) forms part of the largest pilot organisation in the world, International AOPA, and becoming a member of AOPA does make you become more of an integral part of the private flying movement in this country. Despite the slightly misleading name, membership of AOPA is open to any pilot and not restricted to just those pilots who are also aircraft owners as well as pilots. I know this unfortunate misconception has in the past put off many UK pilots from becoming members of AOPA. Your membership of AOPA helps give private flying a useful and authoritative voice to argue its own case in the UK and, as is becoming more and more important these days, also within the European aviation authorities.

Most European countries, and many other states worldwide, have their own AOPAs, all of which are affiliated to the international body IAOPA, the membership of which totals well over 400,000 pilots. As a member of AOPA UK you get the AOPA UK house magazine, Light Aviation and you will also receive newsletters that help keep you up to date with what is happening within the British private flying scene. AOPA offers members a legal first aid service for any aviation related problem. You can also, as a member, apply for an 'Aircrew Card'. This identifies you as a pilot and can be used to get discounts at various hotels and other places. AOPA UK also has links with car hire companies that offer members special rates, insurance companies (aviation, car, house and life) and finance companies. Overall AOPA endeavours to make flying more useful, safer, and less expensive and more fun. Becoming an International Partner Member of the American parent AOPA organisation gives you access to AOPA's Internet database of aviation information as well as a subscription to their AOPA Pilot magazine and several other privileges. Other national AOPAs also have their own membership privileges.

True to Type

Owners' clubs or Type clubs are certainly useful organisations to belong to if you are an aircraft owner, and they can frequently be helpful even if you just habitually fly the same type of aircraft even if you don't own one. Many of these clubs publish regular newsletters that keep you in the picture concerning new developments, snags that may have been encountered by other pilots, solutions for some of these snags, maintenance tips and so on. These clubs often organise meetings or fly-ins too and these can offer wonderful opportunities to meet people with interests (in the aviation field at least) which are similar to your own. Flying in to attend these meetings (many of which are held in conjunction with similar clubs in other European countries) is also an excellent way of encouraging yourself to do something different and possibly a little more adventurous with your aeroplane than is your usual won't. Active groups of this nature have been formed in Britain around many types of aircraft, including vintage Pipers, Aeroncas, the American Aviation/Grumman/ Gulfstream range, Robins and others.

Home for Home Builders

The LAA is the backbone of all the home-building activities that go on in this country and if you decide, after reading Chapter 8, that you want to make a move into aircraft ownership via that route, and then you will certainly become a member of LAA. This does not by any means imply that other pilots who fly factory built aircraft are not also welcome as members. Quite the contrary. Membership of the LAA is another way of learning a great deal about your hobby of light aircraft flying from what may, to you, be a fresh and fascinating angle. If you are harbouring any dark thoughts at the back of your mind about spending all your spare time out in the garage or garden shed with saws and tin snips and pliers, or plastic, adhesives and glass paper, you owe it to yourself to become a LAA member. That should sort things out for you one way or another. You may begin to marvel at the long suffering dedication of these crazy plane building people (and their even longer suffering partners) and go off the whole idea. It is far better to do this, if you are going to, before you have committed yourself too far technically or financially into the home build project. On the other hand you may well find yourself gradually becoming unable to resist the idea of weekends and long evenings of creative craftsmanship, after your normal work is over; seemingly endless hours of wood and metalwork, gluing, painting and polishing. Long hours certainly, but hours which do eventually culminate in the ineffable satisfaction of taking to the air in something that you have created with your own two hands.

All around the country there are branches (called 'Struts') of the LAA at which local members get together to discuss the relative merits of different home built designs, share experiences, make contact with the engineers and inspectors who oversee all building projects, and generally enjoy each others' company. I've come across some enthusiasts who actually join the LAA and build their own aircraft, even before they took the trouble to qualify for a PPL, and I have enjoyed being a member of the LAA for many years, without ever having had the courage to start building anything more enterprising than a model aeroplane. LAA has space for, and welcomes, all types of members, flyers and non-flyers.

Sky Watch Civil Air Patrol

Once you have logged a few hours as P1 and feel reasonably confident that you can fly safely while giving attention at the same time to things outside the aircraft, you might consider joining the Civil Air Patrol (CAP). This is a voluntary pilots' organisation dedicated to helping services such as the police and coastguard when search and observation from the air can be useful to them. Pilot members of the CAP look out for people or property in danger such as children being blown out to sea on inflatable craft; or scramblers who have become stuck on cliffs. They search for lost hikers or mountaineers, disturbed people, missing aircraft, small boats etc.

There are two categories of pilot in the Sly Watch Civil Air Patrol, 'Basic' and 'Responder'. The minimum qualification to join Sky Watch as a pilot is a PPL or NPPL together with a radio licence. Once the application is approved by Sky Watch headquarters, the applicant will be assigned to the nearest Sky Watch Civil Air Patrol Unit and awarded the 'basic' category. There are CAP units in many areas of Great Britain and you will almost certainly find there is one not far from your home base. As a Basic CAP pilot you will be expected to 'observe and report' during your recreational flying and you may voluntarily carry out patrol flights not below 2,000 feet minimum separation distance (msd). Any incident you happen to spot should be reported to the emergency services via the nearest ATC unit. You will also be encouraged to take part in Sky Watch training exercises that will improve your flying, navigation and radio communication skills.

Pilots who have logged more than 250 flying hours (of which 200 hours must be P1) may apply to their Sky Watch unit chief pilot to be promoted to the 'responder' category. Before becoming a 'responder' you need to have taken part in several training exercises and have demonstrated that you are able to carry out complex search patterns below 2,000 feet msd, but not below 500 feet msd. Responder pilots whose names are on their CAP unit call out list may expect to receive requests (via their unit chief pilot) from the RAF Aeronautical Rescue Co-ordination Centre (ARCC) and their local HM Coastguard Maritime Rescue Co-ordination Centre (MRCC) to fly air observation sorties when dedicated air search assets are in short supply. There is of course no obligation to react to such requests if other personal or work commitments get in the way; your service as a CAP pilot is always purely voluntary.

Air searches by Sky Watch aircraft only take place during daylight hours and over land. However, during a coastal search you are permitted fly the aircraft over the sea as long as you remain within gliding distance of the shore. The final go/no go decision is always that of the aircraft commander.

Just like other recognised voluntary organisations such as Mountain Rescue and the Royal National Lifeboats Institution, Sky Watch CAP has established standards of training and operational efficiency. There is a Sky Watch Operations Manual which member pilots can use as a self help tool to learn air observation and search techniques so that if they are called upon to perform a particular task they can carry it out effectively. On signing up to the 'Active List', you will be expected to agree to various commitments including keeping a look out (whenever you safely and conveniently can) during the course of your general flying and carrying out air observation flights in your area, preferably with an observer, looking for persons or property which may be at risk, for example in remote countryside and coastal areas, lakes and rivers. You would of course then report any incident seen during these flights to Air Traffic Control for a land line 999 call to the Emergency Services

One valuable by product of the Sky Watch Civil Air Patrol has been the generation of a better public image of private flying because of positive media coverage of CAP activities. Sky Watch was not started with public relations for General Aviation in mind, but if it helps to change the man (and woman) in the streets view of private flying that can only be a good thing.

Association for Woman Pilots

There is another British pilots' association which will be of interest only to what is regrettably a small proportion of the pilots who are likely to read this book. It is also the only pilots' association in the UK whose membership is gender limited. I am referring here to the British Women Pilots' Association (BWPA). One of the aims of the BWPA is to turn flying into less of a minority interest activity for women, and another is to do all they can to remove the so called 'glass ceiling' which tends to limit career prospects for female pilots. Since it is not one of the aims of this book to deal in any detail with commercial flying matters, I shall not pursue that second objective any farther here. It is worth pointing out, however, that many women who are private pilots, and whose aim is to continue flying for pleasure rather than to make a career in aviation, do find membership of the BWPA both useful and interesting. The BWPA celebrated its half century of existence in 2005 and now has local branches active in various parts of the country. The BWPA is a great help in bringing women pilots together to discuss their common interests.

Agricultural Aviation and Aerodrome Ownership

If you happen to be engaged in agriculture, and particularly if you regularly fly to and from farm strips rather than international airports, then you could well find that the Flying Farmers' Association (FFA) would be an organisation of considerable interest to you. One of its main functions is to assist FFA members in the exchange of ideas, problems and solutions on all manner of themes that affect farm flying. These can include subjects ranging from planning permits to petrol pumps, set aside to strip mowing and noise abatement to uninvited visitors. Again this is very much a minority interest association, but as such it can and does offer its members a good specialised service that is difficult for them to obtain from anywhere else. Similarly, the Aerodrome Owners' Association is not one that will be of interest to more than a few of the private pilots who read this volume, but for those who happen to be involved in the ownership or operation of an aerodrome, the AOA offers a wealth of shared knowledge and experience that could well turn out to be of inestimable value.

Chapter 7
Pilots' Playthings

GPS Navigators

The methods by which aircraft have been navigated through the skies have evolved steadily throughout the first 100 years of powered flight's history. Map reading and dead reckoning were complemented first by astro-navigation, and then simple radio beacons and airborne loop aerials brought a new accuracy to navigation when both the surface and the stars were obscured. Radar in all its various forms, directional radio beams, VHF Omni-directional range beacons (VOR) and instrument landing systems (ILS) were all developed over the years to improve navigational accuracy and increase safety. The latest, and possibly the largest single step in aerial navigation technology came during the 1990s. This was the launch into orbit of the United States NavStar satellites to provide the basis for their Global Positioning System (GPS). Almost simultaneously the then Soviet Union launched another constellation of satellites which is still being maintained and operated by Russia and serves their Global Navigation Satellite System (GLONASS). The European Union has also made considerable progress towards its own independent third constellation of 30 navigation satellites which will provide the Galileo European satellite navigation system. Two Galileo satellites were already in orbit in 2008 but the entry into service of the system has, for political and financial reasons, been delayed several times. China already has a limited three-satellite navigation system known as Beidou and has a military satellite navigation system called Compass under development but Compass is unlikely to go into service until well after Galileo.

The principles of these satellite systems are too complex to describe in detail here and sufficient magazine articles and text books on the subject already exist to satisfy the interested reader. Suffice it to say that GPS (with or without GLONASS and Galileo) has the potential to offer pilots a navigation system of hitherto unmatched accuracy. This usefulness is already being developed into the field of instrument landing and this already is providing, in many countries of the world, officially approved instrument approach facilities at airfields where none ever before existed.

Because (although US politicians have promised not to do so) the risk has always existed that the United States authorities could switch off or degrade the accuracy of their GPS at any time, there has been an understandable reluctance within many civil aviation authorities outside the United States to allow its unrestricted use by civil aircraft as their sole or even a main means of navigation. Once Galileo is up and running (and extremely unlikely ever to be deliberately denied to users at the same time as the American GPS were to be shut down) satellite navigation will almost inevitably become an accepted and fully approved method of aerial navigation, certainly for the light aircraft that are operated by the private pilot readers of this book. But (and that is a big but) nothing contained in this section should be taken as implying that any pilot has authority to navigate within the airspace of any particular state either solely, or partly, by reference to satellite derived data. You must always check the current legal situation for yourself. This is constantly changing territory.

The signals sent out by the navigation satellites require special receivers before you can put them to use and a wide and growing selection of these receivers has come onto the aviation market since the GPS first became operational. In addition GPS has entered many other market sectors where receivers designed for marine use, for surveying, road navigation etc. are all available. The price of a basic aviation GPS receiver has tumbled since the early days of GPS, and some of the relatively low cost receivers designed for aviation purposes now incorporate many sophisticated and useful special functions. Many of the non aviation GPS receivers tend to be priced at a mere fraction of the cheapest aviation versions, but none of these offer the accuracy or all the facilities that are essential for a pilot user and which make GPS such a versatile navigation system for light aircraft. All three satellite navigation systems, GPS, GLONASS and Galileo have the ability to pinpoint your position anywhere around the world to within a few meters and both military and civilian pilots as well as all the other users, can make use of all the benefits of the system's extremely high precision.

Some of the early GPS receivers worked well enough technically but had distinctly user unfriendly pilot interfaces. It was nice to know that the GPS avionics always had the aircraft's position accurately plotted, but it would have been even better if the pilot had been able to find out too. If the design of a SatNav receiver increases pilot workload or makes it difficult for him or her to maintain situational awareness, accidents are likely to happen. Fortunately, the manufacturers have listened to their customers and current models of SatNav avionics are much more user-friendly than their predecessors, now having been designed to reduce pilot workload rather than bamboozle pilots. The key to safe flying with SatNav is for pilots to be completely familiar with the receivers and displays they are using. This can be quite tricky, if only because most units have a lot of sometimes abstruse features and functions. The secret is to make use of the user manual to master the basics of basic navigation with the unit you are using, and to learn gradually how all its other functions work. Time spent in the office or at home with the receiver in simulation mode (assuming it is not a panel mounted one) is time well spent. This is one area in which the slogan of 'when all else fails, read the instructions' definitely does not apply. Read the instructions first, otherwise you'll join the ranks of the many pilots who know how to press the 'Go To' button on their GPS, but know virtually nothing else of the dozens of other ways in which it could be invaluably helpful to their flying.

The Skymap IIIC is an excellent GPS moving map with a colour display screen, but like most portable GPS units, it can be difficult to install it where it is easy to read, doesn't obstruct the pilot's view and doesn't give rise to a spider's web of cables in the cockpit.

Aviation SatNav receivers come in a wide variety of specifications, VFR only and IFR approved (in those states where GPS IFR is itself approved) both as panel mounted units and as handheld receivers. The simplest of the handheld aviation units will provide a screen display of latitude and longitude (and height, though this last is generally less precise than the latitude and longitude) and have a database into which you must yourself enter all the way points you wish to use; aerodromes, turning points, towns, nav aids or anything else you choose. The typical aviation satellite receiver has an array of buttons to press which will enable you to enter and memorise a route using whichever of these way points you need, or instantly to give you heading and distance to 'Go To' any of them directly. It will display your course, track, ground speed, time en route, estimated time of arrival and many other bits of navigational information, depending on the design of receiver and the way you program it. Most GPS units however have the ability to accept professionally compiled database cartridges, such as the Jeppesen ones, which include an enormous fund of aviation information about each aerodrome and its facilities, each nav aid, reporting point and so on, over vast areas of the earth's surface. To keep this database information accurate and up to date it is necessary to change them or download up dates for them regularly. New databases can be purchased and slotted into these receivers, or in many cases, up-dated data can be downloaded from the Internet directly into the receivers. The high cost of constantly updating the information in them is reflected by the charges made for the up dated databases but despite that, it is highly desirable for any flyer, including VFR pilots, to maintain these databases current, as frequently as possible, and this is absolutely essential if they are being used for IFR operations.

Probably the best set-up for any GA aeroplane is a glass cockpit where GPS moving map display is only one of the options available to the pilot. This dual Avidyne glass cockpit is fitted to a Cirrus SR-22 single engine aircraft.

Even the most enthusiastic users of GPS have to admit that there are certain limitations to the usefulness and reliability of satellite navigation, but fortunately these drawbacks are reducing all the time. As is the case with VORs, NDBs, VHF radios and virtually all navigation aids, there remains a small possibility of the Global Positioning System breaking down, being jammed, or otherwise interfered with, so it cannot be relied upon implicitly for navigation under all circumstances. And if your receiver is a straightforward VFR one then it won't have WAAS integrity or RAIM (Receiver Autonomous Integrity Monitoring) which is designed to raise a flag whenever anything happens that makes it dangerous for you to trust the navigation data coming from the receiver. Without RAIM built into your receiver, you must remember that there's no warning if a satellite goes off tune or has its signals compromised by interference, so don't ever depend solely on GPS. Keeping your eye firmly on where you are, on an old fashioned paper chart, is a good insurance policy against finding yourself being let down unexpectedly by these mystic signals from inner space.

Where panel space is limited or cost an important factor the smaller size and lower price of the still very versatile Garmin GNS 430 make it an attractive fit for many GA aircraft. This one is installed in a Cessna 180 single.

The clear and colourful navigation screen display on a GNS 430.

GPS is particularly vulnerable to jamming, either deliberate of intentional, because the receivers are extremely sensitive. They need to be in order to pick up the extremely weak signals that come from the orbiting satellites. A relatively low powered jammer transmitting within the GPS frequency band can overwhelm GPS signals over a wide area, up to as far out as a radius of 100 kilometres with just one watt of radiated jamming power. And that is a pretty weak transmitted jamming signal when you think that a typical Mode C transponder can pump out hundreds of watts. GPS receivers are so sensitive that cases of unintentional jamming have been reported from such sources as VHF/UHF television antenna pre-amplifiers and even TV transmitter aerial masts. Jamming is by not the only possible cause that can make a GPS receiver deliver false positional data. Signals from the GPS satellites can be corrupted, too few satellites can be visible at certain times for them to deliver an accurate position and the receivers themselves, like all man-made equipment, are not infallible. The fears about deliberate jamming are probably exaggerated despite worries over terrorist activity, but inadvertent jamming is a problem, and GPS systems can malfunction. To be a prudent navigator you should constantly be using all available means of navigation to cross check your position. RNAV, VOR/DME, ADF and looking out of the cockpit to identify landmarks periodically are all sensible options.

That said, my own experience has been that, ever since I first invested in a GPS moving map system back in 1992, I have been getting continuous and reliable information from it each and every time I have used it. And once the European Galileo system is operational and running in parallel with the United States GPS, the reliability of any aviation SatNav receiver capable of picking up and using data signals from both satellite systems should be virtually 100%.

Moving Maps

Even satellite navigation receivers that do not have an integral moving map display all are supplied complete with an output connection which enables them to feed positional data into another unit (such as a PDA pocket computer, hand held PC, notebook or laptop) that can display a moving map. Even more convenient are the many units that incorporate the GPS receiver, the moving map and data display screen all in one unit. This map display can be almost anything between a relatively crude sketch map of the area being over flown showing, in white lines on a black or green background, the approximate line of the coast and the positions of airfields, nav aids and large towns to a sophisticated bit of electronic cartography. Some SatNav moving maps are a little more detailed, and include airspace boundaries and other relevant aviation data, but the most expensive of the genre can display much greater degree of detail right up to showing a full colour on screen representation of an ICAO half million aeronautical chart. All this extremely detailed information is derived from database cartridges and, like the databases referred to above; the information used to make these moving maps appear on screen must be maintained up to date if you want them to remain useful and safe for you to navigate by.

A GPS moving map makes accurate aerial navigation childishly simple. That, and the way in which you can so easily interpret the information, does sometimes have an unfortunate side effect that you should do your best to guard against. It can all too easily tempt the unwary VFR pilot into flying in weather conditions that are really beyond his or her flying ability. In poor visibility you do feel so much safer knowing exactly where you are, knowing for certain that you haven't drifted a few miles off course, closer than is healthy to controlled airspace, mountains or perhaps a TV transmitter mast. You can probably see them all marked clearly on your moving map and you know your precise position relative to each of them. But always bear in mind that your trusty GPS could let you down. Before you get carried away by technology and find yourself out of your depth, just take a moment to visualise how you would feel if that marvellous little map screen (or even the basic GPS receiver navigation data screen) suddenly went blank. Would you still feel quite so comfortable hurtling blindly on through the clag then? If the honest answer to that question is in the negative, then you owe it to yourself and to your passengers to resist the temptation to press on. Don't let yourself be lulled into a false sense of security by these useful, but potentially evanescent, electronic lines on a little glass screen.

The Garmin GNS 530 is an excellent example of a panel mounted multi purpose GPS navigator. Two of these are seen here fitted into the panel of a Lear 25.

This GNS 530 screen is shown with terrain avoidance and warning display which alerts and warns the pilot of potential terrain and obstacle conflicts along the flight path.

The GNS 530 showing a basic display of airspace and navigational information.

GPS receivers come in a wide variety of permutations. As mentioned, they are available with integral moving maps, and also as independent receivers you can couple to slave map units. Hand held GPS receivers with or without maps, moving map programs to load onto laptop PCs, large and small panel-mounted GPS sets, some incorporating conventional Nav and Com receivers, some coupled to other cockpit displays such as thunderstorm plotters and Traffic Collision Avoidance Systems (TCAS), and many other variations on similar themes, also exist. Not all of these will be ideally suited to the type of flying you want to do, nor to the type of aircraft you use for most of your flying. The GPS that best suits an aircraft owner may not suit a pilot who normally flies aircraft hired from flying clubs. A laptop PC based moving map may be all right in a large cockpit, but very difficult to cope with in a cramped one. You may be prepared to accept a spider's web of wires connecting GPS, cigar lighter, antenna and pocket PC display unit, but other pilots would loathe flying with that kind of tangle of cables in the cockpit. It pays to check the current catalogues carefully, and to make sure you haven't missed something that would more perfectly dovetail in with your particular requirements and your budget. Manufacturers are coming out with new and improved designs all the time in this fast-moving and exciting branch of avionics.

Don't be persuaded by their lower prices to buy a GPS that's designed for automotive, sailing, biking or hill-walking use and then try to use it for navigation in an aircraft. These units are not at all satisfactory for aviation use, with databases containing no aeronautical information.

Whatever you do, though, don't allow the substantially lower prices charged for GPS units designed for the marine, hiking, biking, automotive or hill walking markets lure you into buying one of these for aviation use. They are totally unsuited for that purpose, have databases that don't contain aeronautical information and are downright dangerous to navigate with in the air.

Just around the corner as this edition of this book goes to press are the next developments in SatNav for pilots. For a start there is the Wide Area Augmentation System (WAAS) which is the American version of a system known internationally as a Satellite Based Augmentation System (SBAS), because the system provides augmentation signals from satellites. Work is underway in the USA, Europe, Japan and India on versions of SBAS that will broadcast ICAO

standard signals, and so provide seamless global coverage. The FAA faced a number of technical and program challenges during the development of WAAS, but the system eventually came into commercial service. Europe is progressing towards commissioning the European Geostationary Navigation Overlay System (EGNOS) and India and Japan have started work on their compatible systems. All four SBASs are being designed for en route, terminal, non precision approach and a new type of "approach with vertical guidance" which should mean lower minima, hence higher airport usability in many cases. A network of

Even the more up market hiking and biking GPS receivers like this Etrex Legend are unsuitable for serious use in the cockpit.

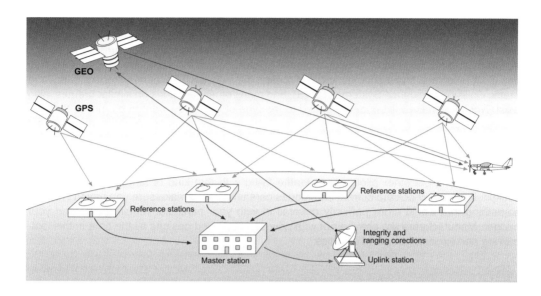

WAAS reference stations monitors GPS signals and relays data to a master station, which assesses signal validity, computes corrections and creates the WAAS message. It sends this to a ground uplink station for relay to geostationary satellites orbiting over the equator. These satellites rebroadcast the message on the GPS L1 frequency; their signals cover a hemisphere, except for Polar Regions.

The WAAS signal contains correction and integrity data as well as ranging signals. The correction data allows the receiver to compensate for satellite clock and orbital position errors, as well as for the signal delays caused by the ionosphere. The resulting horizontal and vertical accuracy is usually better than 2 metres. The integrity data is used as described above, and solves the availability problem with RAIM. The ranging signals make the geostationary satellites look like GPS satellites and this also helps boost availability of service.

The Local Area Augmentation System (LAAS) is the American name for the system known elsewhere as a Ground Based Augmentation System (GBAS) because the system provides augmentation signals from ground stations. The ultimate goal with LAAS is to support all categories of precision approach, and eventually surface movement guidance. With LAAS, a ground reference station at the airport broadcasts satellite ranging corrections via VHF to aircraft within 25-30nm, so a single system serves all runways. The cost of a single LAAS is forecast to be less than the cost of an ILS, which serves only one runway.

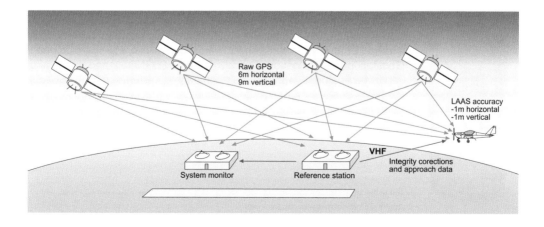

Trials in the US and elsewhere going back to the mid 1990s have shown that LAAS can deliver accuracy that can be used for Category III (Low Visibility Approaches) approaches. However, as is the case with WAAS, accuracy is easy while integrity of the all important satellite signals remains the challenge. Future developments will depend on the very complex integration of GPS, Galileo and GLONASS signals, augmentation systems and avionics to meet the necessary navigation performance standards. The accuracy of the receiver databases is of great importance when it comes to precision approaches, as of course is the design of SatNav procedures. If it is your intention to use your receiver eventually for IFR navigation, then it is a WAAS capable receiver you must be looking at. These are now available at little or no extra cost compared with basic GPS units bit if you do buy a basic GPS at least check that it can be upgraded to use with WAAS (or EGNOS) and what that is likely to cost. And talking of costs, remember that the true cost of SatNav doesn't stop with purchase of the receiver. There are installation costs for a panel mounted one, and integrating one of these with HSI, CDI, autopilot, Stormscope, TCAS etc can make that quite a substantial sum. Then there is the cost of learning the unit yourself (or training other pilots to use it efficiently) and finally the cost of regular updates for the databases. These costs even apply to the private pilot owner of a light aircraft, who will have to spend some time in the air (and maybe even pay for the services of an instructor) to learn how to use the receiver properly. Don't even think about flying an approach under IMC until you are completely familiar with the equipment. It isn't quite as straightforward as tuning in an ILS and flying down the glideslope.

With its 7 inch diagonal colour screen this AvMap EKP-IV knee mounted GPS provides the pilot with an unusually large and easily read moving map display.

The Honeywell Bendix-King AV80R is another of the many GPS receivers designed for general aviation use. This one has the additional facility of a database that also contains road navigation and a speaker that gives prompts so you don't have to take your eyes off the road while driving

Handheld VHF Radios

In Chapter 2, while we were considering how some pilots need to overcome a little diffidence before they feel comfortable about making proper use of the aircraft radio, the wide range of portable aircraft band VHF receivers that are now available on the market was mentioned. These radios (also known as 'scanners') can be very useful for listening in to aircraft transmissions and familiarising yourself with radiotelephony procedures but they are an entirely different type of radio from the hand-held VHF radios being discussed here. These are more properly known as 'transceivers' and are combined VHF receivers and transmitters. They normally have a frequency range that spans the entire aircraft VHF band, from 118.000 MHz to 137.000 MHz. Frequently a navigation facility is built in which also permits use of the unit as a VOR receiver, complete with a Course Deviation Indicator (CDI) display on the unit's LCD screen. In some models it is possible to use the Nav VOR facility simultaneously with listening out and transmitting on the VHF radio, but on other types of transceiver this dual function is not available.

This King KX99 (seen here slipped partially into its protective cover) is a typical handheld VHF radio transceiver that comes complete with a VOR navigation facility and CDI display.

Pilots generally purchase handheld transceivers either as a backup radio, to be kept in your flight kit or the glove box of the aeroplane in case of radio or electrical failure, or to monitor ATIS, tower, VOLMET or other aviation frequencies while on the ground. While many pilots probably justify the purchase of a handheld by talking about its emergency use, most handhelds probably spend most of their operational time scanning local ATC frequencies while lying on a wing or cowling, office desk or workbench.

Pilots of microlights and many home-built aircraft use them as their main VHF radio for all normal radiotelephony (RT) in their aircraft. Many other pilots who fly aircraft equipped with one or more panel mounted VHF radios, also carry a hand-held transceiver with them in their pilot case, mainly as an emergency back up in case electrical failure in the aircraft denies them the use of the built in aircraft radios. It is not all that unusual for a panel mounted VHF radio to become unusable for one reason or another. I have known the aircraft's alternator to fail and after that, as soon as all the power from the battery (approx 30 minutes) has drained away, the aircraft's radios are entirely useless. Occasionally the failure of a relay, or the sticking of a microphone button, is enough to put a built in VHF radio out of action. Even a defective frequency selector can leave a pilot unable to change to the channel required at the time. If any such misfortune ever strikes while you are flying, you will be very glad indeed of a hand-held radio if you have one with you in the cockpit. These hand-held transceivers are also of potentially life saving value in the event of a ditching (or even a forced landing in desolate country) when a one of them can provide a vital channel of communication with the search and rescue services. They're also used by some pilots to close flight plans after engine shutdown or to ask for start-up clearance and to receive IFR clearances before engine start.

Which Model Suits Your Flying?

Whether you need any of the optional features (or whether you even need a handheld transceiver at all) depends on the type of flying you do (IFR or VFR) and how you intend to use the radio. Do you intend using it solely as an emergency backup transceiver or just to monitor aviation frequencies? To help you make up your mind which handheld to buy, I would suggest you consider the following.

If you fly only VFR and seldom if ever want to listen to aviation frequencies while on the ground, perhaps you don't need a handheld at all. Actual emergency and backup uses for a handheld transceiver fortunately don't occur very often for VFR pilots. Radio contact isn't required at many small airfields, or nor is it mandatory anywhere in an emergency. If you are flying under VFR then, you simply just land at the nearest suitable place, field or airfield. The main backup use for a VFR pilot's handheld is therefore little more than being handy for communicating with search and rescue aircraft from the ground if you are ever fortunate (and unfortunate) enough to be the survivor of an accident in a remote area. That isn't a bad reason to own a handheld, but even then it is unlikely that you would be able to talk to SAR aircraft that were any more than about ten miles away from your ground position. There are probably more important survival kit items for you to have on board, if the thought of crash landing in a remote area is one that really worries you. If you want to be able to eavesdrop on the VHF radio chatter at air shows or monitor ATC for fun from home but don't have a need to transmit, you can probably get by with a less expensive scanning receiver, instead of a transceiver handheld. However, if you do have a use for a transmitter and can reasonably follow the directions in the manual, any one of the handheld transceivers will make a pretty good scanner/receiver.

On the other hand, if you fly IFR you should make sure that the handheld you buy has 5 watt peak and 1.5 watt continuous output power, and if you own your own aircraft, you should consider having an external antenna adapter fitted in the cockpit. The built in little antennas don't give handhelds anything like their maximum reception and transmission range. Only use of the handheld through the aircraft's com antennas will achieve that. It is also useful to keep a suitable headset adapter and push to talk switch handy. With a headset, not only will you be more likely to be able to hear ATC more clearly despite the noise of the aircraft engine, but ground stations and other aircraft can understand you much more clearly via the headset's microphone than over the handheld's little built in microphone.

A rechargeable battery pack in a handheld is not really essential unless you expect to use the radio fairly regularly to listen to aviation frequencies at home or at the airfield. Rechargeables are really designed for pilots who use their radios frequently and for long periods of time. A rechargeable battery's storage life is usually about 30-90 days whereas non-rechargeable alkaline batteries can hold their charge for well over a year when kept for emergency use only. And if you have rechargeable you must be pretty diligent in keeping these regularly recharged or you should have an extra alkaline battery pack available for emergencies, just in case sod's law applies and you find the rechargeable power pack is empty when your emergency decides to turn up.

Some of the selling features of these radios seem to me to be rather more sales gimmicks than features of real use to pilots. I wouldn't pay extra just to have a special emergency 121.500 button. With this feature you can select 121.500 by simply pressing one or two buttons. But you could simply tap 1-2-1-5-0 on the keypad and get the same result and I don't believe that cutting out two or three key presses is going to make a life or death difference to you, even in an emergency. Similarly, some handhelds offer what they call duplex communications mode allowing you to use a com frequency at the same time as you are navigating with the VOR function. That isn't a thing you would need to do every other day, is it? In fact, now that most pilots have GPS available, is the transceiver's VOR feature of all that much interest to you itself? Another seemingly attractive feature is the ability some transceivers have to play back to you the last 20 seconds of received transmissions. Initially that sounds like a nice idea but I wonder if it is really a practical idea. In real life it is very seldom you would want to play back what you've heard? If you can't make out an instruction from ATC surely it is easier to ask ATC to, 'say again' rather than to fiddle around getting your handheld to play back a recording. Then there are transceivers that offer the rather useless ability to listen in to NOAA (non-aviation) weather channel broadcasts in the United States, which are not even available anywhere in Europe. I wouldn't choose a handheld especially for the ability to keep more than 50 frequencies in its memory either. There probably aren't that many aviation VHF frequencies within a 100nm range of your home airfield anyway. On the other hand for pilots flying in Europe it just might be worth going for one with 8.33 kHz frequency spacing, ready for the day when these frequencies come into use in lower airspace.

The ICOM IC-A6E is a useful handheld, relatively compact, lightweight and inexpensive. It lacks the VOR facility but this is available in the IC-A24E.

A hand held transceiver's power can come from a cigar lighter socket in the aircraft or from an internal battery pack. This can be of the rechargeable variety, or if the unit is to be used solely as an emergency stand by, then an alkaline battery is probably better, since it holds its charge for a much longer period than a rechargeable. Since a hand held has lots of other valuable potential uses though, I feel it would be a pity if you were to keep yours solely for use in emergencies. It frequently comes in handy on the ground, not just to eavesdrop on airline pilot chatter but (if you are in a favoured area) to get VOLMET broadcast weather information. At busy airfields where start up clearance is required, you can use your hand held transceiver for this purpose to save the drain on the aircraft batteries. (These have to supply not just the VHF radio as soon as you switch the master switch on, but also the gyros etc.) While you are waiting for the previous pilot to return with the club or group aircraft, you can get on with something else useful whilst keeping half an ear open for the 'rejoining' call to come through on the hand held, instead of simply sitting aimlessly waiting for the aircraft to turn up.

Restricted Range

The performance of hand held sets in the air has become much more effective since the early models first appeared but they still have their limitations. Their range is limited by their output transmission power to a maximum radius of approximately 20nm and some become unreadable by ground stations just 15nm away. Even that is not attainable unless the batteries are well charged and the aircraft is fairly high; from around 1,500 feet you are lucky if you can contact a ground station any farther off than about 12nm. You can however usually receive ground transmissions (and aircraft transmissions too) from much farther away than that. I have been able to hear ATC through a handheld (connected to an outside antenna) from as far away as 60nm, but they couldn't hear anything at all from me at that range. The VOR facility works best when the antenna of the hand held is more or less horizontal (and that unfortunately is not the best position for you to read the information on the set's LCD display) and the VOR range is limited to about 25 miles. Both the communications and the navigation range of a hand-held can be improved greatly if it is connected to an external aerial; the foregoing figures refer to its use only with its own antenna.

Keep it Safe

If you do decide to treat yourself to one of these transceivers, please try not to let it get stolen. That is not just because its disappearance might be inconvenient and because if it wasn't insured it would mean you had lost a few hundred pounds worth of equipment. Several of these transceivers seem to have fallen into the wrong hands and some idiots have tried to use them to make spurious pseudo ATC transmissions in attempts to mislead pilots. Fortunately, once the batteries run out the culprits usually don't have any means of recharging them, so the nuisance transmissions cease. I am pretty sure too, that once you have found out what an advantage it is for you to have a hand held transceiver, you certainly wouldn't want to lose it, even if only for selfish but practical personal reasons.

Electronic Calculators etc.

During your flying training days you will initially have been bamboozled by (but hopefully will have eventually come to learn and love) what is still known as a 'flight computer'. It does seem rather odd nowadays, with all these desktop PCs, Macs, notebooks, laptops and pocket PCs around, still to call this archaic looking metal or plastic gadget, with no monitor screen, no keyboard and no electrical power, a computer. That is perhaps one reason you quite often hear it referred to as a 'whiz-wheel' (or occasionally even as a 'Dalton' after the inventor of the original model). Despite its outwardly complicated appearance, the old whiz-wheel turns out to be fairly simple to use, provided you remember the few simple basic rules. It has a lot more than that going for it too, as it never runs out of battery power, has virtually nothing in it that can go wrong and it produces results that are quite accurate enough for any private pilot's navigational purposes.

Despite all these genuine advantages that the whiz-wheel has over its modern electronic counterparts, more and more pilots are now using the new battery powered rivals of the old flight computer. These are actually little more than specialised electronic calculators, which allow pilots to dispense with all the business of sliding pieces of plastic across each other, aligning circular scales and cursers, peering at closely spaced graduation markings on the conversions scales, and calculating triangles of velocities by putting pencil marks on translucent plastic. They seem more familiar to fingers that have become accustomed to pressing buttons on mobile telephones, getting cash out of bank ATMs, keying information into PCs and working with press button radio selectors and GPS receivers. If you have really mastered the traditional (or old fashioned) type of flight computer you may well be of the opinion that real pilots don't use these battery powered toys, and you will soldier on with your good old plastic E6B, ARC-I, CRP-5 or whatever, and never miss the newfangled equivalents. But if you are more accustomed to handling 21st century gizmos, you will probably feel much more comfortable after you switch to one of the electronic variety. Come to think of it, when last did you see a design engineer using a conventional slide rule.

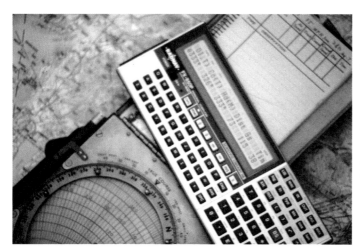

This type of aviation electronic calculator looks very slim and neat compared with the old-fashioned RAF issue Dalton computer shown beside it. Despite that, the battery powered gizmo can do a great deal more for a pilot than the older type of computer ever could.

Like their metal or plastic forebears, these gadgets will work out virtually any aviation conversion; nautical miles, statute miles, kilometres; Fahrenheit/Celsius; gallons/litres; pounds/kilograms etc, and they do so at the touch of a couple of buttons and then display the results clearly and unmistakably on a liquid crystal screen display (LCD). They also solve triangles of velocities and work out headwind and crosswind components, as well as headings and groundspeeds, without using sliding scales and chinagraph pencil marks. Also, in addition to performing all the calculations that the old whiz-wheel will do, these electronic ones can also act as stopwatches or timers, will calculate your aircraft centre of gravity and warn you when it is time to switch from one fuel tank to another. They can also be used for any non aviation mathematical calculation you might want to work out. Although their prices have reduced considerably since they were introduced, the electronic versions are still rather more expensive than the equivalent mechanical ones, but the price ranges tend to overlap, with low cost electronics now being less expensive than top of the range mechanical slide rule ones. They run on standard dry cell batteries which last for many hours of use (but are of course always liable to let you down at the most awkward time) and are slim enough to fit into a shirt pocket or even clip into the ring binder of your flight guide. Like their forerunners they all take a bit of getting used to, but once you become familiar with the electronic programs and how to use them, your old circular slide rule flight computer is liable to start gathering dust.

Sporty's electronic E6B-F calculator can, as shown here, clip neatly inside the ring binder of an The UK Flight Guide and so always be to hand in the cockpit or on the flight planning table.

Electronic Checklists

Similar in general appearance to these electronic calculators, but designed for a totally different purpose, are electronic checklists. These require to have a special data cartridge inserted for whichever type of aircraft you are flying, and once this is done they prompt you through the correct sequence for all the checklists used on that particular model of aircraft. Pre-flight, pre-start, emergency, pre-landing checks etc, are all there and data cartridges are available for a wide variety of light aircraft. Each item appears on the unit's LCD screen and remains on display there until you carry out the check and press a button to tell the gadget that you have effected the check. It is an excellent way in which pilots who have less than perfect memories can ensure that they don't omit items from their vital actions, and it is, I reckon, slightly less easy to forget something when using one of these than when your eye or your finger skips past one of the items on a printed checklist.

Portable Flight Planners

Much more sophisticated in nature and in programming than these electronic checklists are the navigation and flight planning programs which have been written to run on hand held PDAs, notebooks and pocket PCs. Leaving the enormous versatility of the basic computer still fully available, the flight planning programs consist of databases which contain an enormous volume of aviation facts and figures. For example, for each of the hundreds of aerodromes in the database the precise latitude/longitude position is stored, together with such things as: ICAO code; all VHF frequencies; phone numbers; runway directions, lengths and surface type; altitude; lighting; types of instrument approach; ILS frequencies and idents, etc. Naturally, since they are based on much more powerful electronic circuitry than the electronic calculators described above, these organiser units also take easily within their stride the computation of track, heading, groundspeed and time, and can do all the relevant conversions, including IAS/RAS/TAS etc. It is often possible to programme in details of the aircraft you fly, and this enables the organiser to work out for you the fuel you are going to burn, flight costs, weight and balance calculations. Many of them can even give worldwide sunrise and sunset times. Some databases of this type are designed more for IFR than VFR operations, and these include all airways, MSAs, SIDs, STARs and so on; others have been programmed primarily with VFR flyers in mind. It is as well not to get involved with a program that is any more complicated (and more expensive to maintain its database up to date) than you really require. Certain versions of this type of organiser program come ready to be coupled to a GPS receiver. These have the capacity to display on the organiser screen a miniature moving map based on all the navigation data contained in the basic database.

Private Met Office

Another piece of electronic gadgetry that appeals to some pilots is known as a home weather station. This, once you have installed it, complete with its ancillary anemometer and other sensors, enables you to read from its LCD screen the wind speed and direction, ambient temperature, wind chill factor, barometric pressure and even the present time and date, all at the touch of a button or two. You can, if you wish, connect the weather Station to a PC and it will then summarise and store all the collected data for graphing, and recall at will. This could be a fascinating gizmo for the pilot with other reasons beyond flying for being interested in the weather, but now that the Met Office has made so much aviation weather data available free of charge on the Internet, I don't see many private pilots choosing to use a home weather station as a substitute for TAFs, METARs and synoptic charts for their pre-flight briefings.

With a home weather station you can have the basic data available but before you fly you still need TAFs and METARs from the Met Office to comply with regulations.

PC Flight Simulators

It is getting close to the stage where one could claim that no pilot's kit is complete without a Personal Computer. Either sitting on a desk, or as a laptop in the cockpit, these gadgets are becoming almost indispensable, and are certainly extremely useful tools (and toys) for pilots. Personal computers can do much more than connect with the Internet, download web pages, run boring old accounts programs, store digital photographs, produce spreadsheets, help designers with CAD, operate as word processors and keep the kids happy with endless games. They can keep many pilots quietly contented for hours too with flight simulator programs. All that you need to join in (apart from the PC and the programs themselves) is a pseudo aircraft control system with a joystick or yoke and rudder pedals plugged into an appropriate port or USB on the PC.

The realism of PC flight simulator programs has been a story of continuous improvement and good as it is, this screen shot of a Cessna 152 climbing away from Orlando Airport lacks some of the realistic detail of more recent programs.

Flight simulator programs fall into several classes. One class essentially comprises all the many 'games' flight simulator programs, involving high-power contemporary or futuristic jet fighters, World War II aircraft or even flimsy World War I planes, in various battle situations. These are much more suitable for entertaining children (of all ages) than they are for training pilots. Another class of program can be much more interesting to pilots and would be pilots. This is the type of PC flight simulator which has a great deal of realistic scenery on screen. These programs often have a wide range of aircraft, from microlights to Boeing 747s, any of which you can select as the one you want to 'fly'. Best known amongst these programs are probably the various versions of Microsoft's Flight Simulator. A huge library of scenery from all parts of the world has now been built up for these, some by the Microsoft Company itself and a vast amount by other programmers. As well as comprehensively covering its homeland of the USA, this program scenery now enables PC pilots to fly, in simulation, into and out of any airport in Europe as well as many of the smaller airfields and airstrips on this side of the Atlantic.

It is very difficult to distinguish whether this is a flight simulator screen shot or a genuine photograph of an actual Boeing 747.

Microsoft Flight Simulator originated as a computer game and was not really designed as a flying training tool but it can, and does, enable pilots of real aeroplanes to learn quite a lot about cross country navigation plus the airfield layouts and local area landmarks around places they have never previously visited. Certain procedural training can also be done with this type of program. A great deal of fun can be had from them too, enabling inexperienced Cessna pilots to learn at least something about, for example, the different handling characteristics of say aerobatic aircraft, or light twins or even airliners. But this program has distinct limitations and some of these simulated aeroplanes are totally unrealistic in many ways. You can, for example, bring an Airbus airliner in to land on a short grass strip if you wish and you appear to encounter no untoward problems. You can sometimes even happily 'fly' unscathed through mountains or buildings, which is not a habit real pilots should be encouraged to do. Yet in other ways these programs can be remarkably realistic. There are many pilots who get a great deal of pleasure out of their simulator flying as well as their actual time in the air. The simulated flying also has the huge advantage that it comes virtually free of charge once the PC and programs have been bought.

Using a PC flight simulator you can enjoy handling types of aircraft (like this Douglas DC3) which respond realistically to your control inputs and which you would be most unlikely ever to fly in real life. You also have the chance to operate in and out of exotic locations (like Honolulu here) which look really authentic on your PC screen.

The representation of specific aircraft instrument panels and avionics has become quite an art form in modern flight simulators. Here is an example of what you might see on a PC monitor when 'flying' a Cessna 172.

There are many other flight simulator programs available for use on PCs, each with its own advantages and drawbacks. The accuracy of the flight characteristics, the detail of the scenery, the realism of weather phenomena, the range of types available to 'fly' on it as well as the cost of the program itself are all factors to consider. So too is the compatibility of the program to the computing equipment you have, and the availability of extras, such as additional types to 'fly' and additional scenery that may include the geographical areas that particularly interest you. With the right PC equipment you can even arrange to hear the voices of the ATC controllers giving instructions as you fly.

'X-Plane' is another of the many relatively lightweight PC flight-simulator programs that is fun to use, but for more serious PC training such as might interest a PPL holder heading for an instrument rating or moving on towards a commercial licence, there are several more sophisticated simulators. Expensive, but among the very best of these, come the 'Elite IFR simulation programs' and their associated flying control equipment and avionics. Other software simulator programs include the 'ASA On Top flight simulator' and ASA's 'Instrument Procedures Trainer'. Some simulators of this type have gained FAA approval in the States and time spent at their controls may be logged there as simulated instrument flying. These more advanced simulators can be configured to represent various specific types of aircraft and their software is fully capable of faithfully replicating the performance of these various types of aircraft. The controls for these programs also vary greatly in price and in realism. In some cases you need to invest in a control console with throttle, flap and undercarriage levers and simulated engine controls. Some of the best of the available controls actually incorporate feedback feel and even vibrations through the stick or yoke, making it very easy to be carried away by the feeling you are actually in the air while still sitting at your favourite PC station. Instrument qualified pilots can use programs of this type to keep their IF skills in practice. Even the private pilot with no immediate intention of going on to obtain an IMC or Instrument Rating, could get a great deal of pleasure out of one of these flight-simulator programs and at the same time learn a great deal about flying on instruments. When the weather has clamped (or the finances have run dry for the month) and real VFR flying is out of the question, simulated VFR on a home computer is often better than nothing. And a keen pilot can also pick up quite a lot of valuable information on how to make the best use of nav aids, even in VFR, by using some of the other PC programs described below.

Other Learning Tools

Less demanding on the PC hardware required, but still giving very useful experience in how to fly on instruments with reference to nav aids, are relatively inexpensive simulator programs like the 'Radio Aids Navigation Tutor (RANT)' by Oddsoft, 'GPS Trainer', and the 'VOR and ADF Familiarisation' program by VORTex. The pilot who has access to a PC is certainly in a position to polish up many navigation and instrument flying skills without spending expensive flying time actually in the air. There are simple programs to teach you the Morse Code, somewhat more complex ones to help you master instrument flying procedures, such as an ADF/RBI Tutor which covers things like NDB holds, track interception, coping with wind and drift, and a VOR Tutor which deals with both OBI and HSI presentations and covers all the IF applications of flying with reference to a VOR. You can run through programs such as these over and over again in front of your PC until the procedures are engrained into your mind. As a consequence, the time taken to pilot yourself through these procedures in the air should be much reduced and the cost of your instrument qualification likewise.

CD-ROM Training Programs

A growing number of aviation training programs are now becoming available on CD-ROM and these have many advantages over the older video tape programs. The new medium makes it so easy to find and repeat sections of the course as required without the endless hit or miss forward and reverse winding of the tape. The new training aids are also interactive, which greatly helps to keep the student's interest concentrated on the task in hand. Pilot's shop catalogues will keep you up to date with the latest versions of these programs, both ab-initio training ones, which are useful to the PPL for revision and keeping abreast of changes in legislation and advanced courses helping PPL holders to develop their skills in new fields.

Computer Based Training Programs

Recent years have seen a wide range of generally very worth while training programs and courses for pilots which are based on CD-ROMs. Oxford Aviation Training in conjunction with the UK Met Office have produced one of the best of these in Aviation Meteorology, an interactive training course covering Met theory, flight briefing and Met Office services, complete with test questions in both JAA and FAA examination paper format. Another of Oxford's CD-ROMs teaches pilots exactly how to get the best out of their Flight Computers (the metal/plastic, not the electronic variety). There are similar courses teaching VHR RTF communications techniques both for VFR and for IFR that are quite enjoyable to work through on a computer and the teaching is probably more easily assimilated this on-screen, interactive way than simply by reading a conventional textbook. ASA also have excellent courses on CD-ROM for pilots wanting to gain an FAA Pilot or Instrument certificates.

For pilots who still haven't fully grasped the hows and whys of their Flight Computer there is a useful Navigation Tutorial training program from Griffon Aviation Software, which takes you through the procedure for whichever whiz-wheel you want to use and then persistently quizzes you about how to work its various functions, until you know you have grasped them all. The same company also publishes a PC program called the PPL Training Kit. Since most readers of this book probably have their PPLs already, I suppose I can only recommend this for revision purposes, or as a present for a PC buff friend of yours who is thinking about learning to fly and might like an easily assimilated, highly graphical, version of the full PPL course to work through with keyboard, mouse and monitor.

Just because you already have a PPL in your pocket doesn't mean that the PPL training DVDs are not for you. They form an excellent way of revising and keeping on top of your basic skills and knowledge, all of which is essential if you are going to continue to enjoy safe flying into the future. Many pilots are more likely to return to freshen up their knowledge of Met or aviation law from a DVD than they are to dust down their old PPL training textbooks from the shelf and thumb through these again. Sets of DVDs are now widely used for computer based training of pilots. Several suppliers have these for the FAA Pilot and Instrument examinations, and the DVD has replaced the training video for most aspects of pilot training. Understandably, considering the ease with which you can go back and repeat a point, or skip forward to reach what you want, compared with the laborious fast-forward and fast reverse that is needed with videos on a VCR. But videos are still on sale, as are audio CD's, covering almost all the subjects mentioned in the book, night flying, Morse, IMC rating, helicopter PPL, multi engine flying and cross country navigation to name but a few. The range of advanced pilot subjects available on DVD is increasing almost monthly, and many are now available for holders of JAA PPLs as well as FAA pilot certificates so it isn't always necessary to learn your advanced flying techniques to a background of American accents and scenery, FAA procedures and exam questions.

PC Logbooks, Flight Planners etc.

There are many other aviation computer programs on the market that have been written specifically for the private flyer. Some can even be downloaded free of charge or as 'shareware' from the Internet. If you fancy backing up the bound paper copy of your flying logbook with an electronic version, you will find many programs for this purpose on the Internet. There are many others available to buy which obviously cost you something, but are probably more sophisticated, and more thoroughly debugged, than some of the 'freeware' and 'shareware' on the Internet. These are available for sale through pilot shops and the usual aviation mail order outlets as well as on the Internet. Most of these logbook programs have the advantage that they let you quickly and easily produce all sorts of specialised data from your log. Once you have flown a few hundred hours in a selection of different aircraft types, things like the number of hours solo time you have logged at night in Cessna 152, can take a lot of searching through pages of written entries. Any PC logbook program worth its salt should be able to give you that sort of information in a flash, as well as fun things like the number of times you have flown with a certain instructor, landed at a given airfield or even list the names of all the airfields you have ever landed at and count in a flash how many places you have visited in your flying career to date.

The number of different ways you can use PCs in connection with private flying seems to grow steadily. Amongst the programs which I have found over the years to be most useful are those written to help you with flight planning. None of these are particularly demanding on PC specification. In principle they are all similar. Each contains a database of aerodrome, nav aid and other way point information, which must of course be kept up to date to guarantee safe and accurate flight plans. Each also contains software that quickly and precisely calculates distances and tracks, allows for wind, climb, descent and other factors, to produce times, groundspeeds, ETAs etc. Some will produce print outs, not only of the flight log (which can even be run off in an ATC acceptable ICAO format) but of GPS coordinates, latitudes and longitudes of all waypoints, frequencies of all VHF stations you might want to use en route, and similar essential or highly desirable information. Even a long and complicated route, which would take for ever to plan in the conventional way with scales, protractors, charts and chinagraph pencils, can be produced in a few seconds by one of these number crunching programs. Many PC flight planning programs have appeared on the market only to disappear again after a few months, but two which have, for very good reasons, stood the test of time are Jeppesen's FliteStar (available in VFR and IFR formats) and the NavBox programs, QuickPlan and ProPlan. These are available in several different formats, some of which can interface with a GPS, and each of which serves its particular purpose very competently. Simpler programs with databases which you are required to fill and maintain by yourself are also available. Some of these are free of charge on aviation sections of the Internet, just waiting for you to download and use them.

Details of most of the items mentioned in this chapter (and of a multitude of other pilots' playthings) are available from pilot shops and aviation supplies catalogues such as AFE, Pooley's, Transair Pilot Shop, LAA Pilot Shop etc.

Chapter 8
The Pilot's Ultimate Plaything

When is Your Own Aeroplane Worthwhile?

There cannot be many people who hold a Private Pilot Licence who have not at least thought about owning their own aeroplane and, if you are one of those few pilots who haven't yet thought about it, you are almost certainly going to start dreaming about it one of these days. Many of us never get beyond the stage of longing and wistfully imagining what it might be like, but quite a few hundred pilots in the UK, and many thousands of PPL holders worldwide, do in fact own their own aeroplanes. Very frequently private aircraft ownership is a perfect example of the heart ruling the head. An elementary exercise in accountancy would prove that many owners would be a great deal better off if they simply contented themselves with flying aircraft that they rented from a local club. However, pilots are really quite fortunate that accountants don't (not yet, at least) completely rule the world, because there are many factors associated with aircraft ownership that just cannot be reduced to simple terms of cash.

It is great to imagine yourself as the owner of a comfortably large, powerful, fast aircraft like this Rockwell 114, but sometimes you have to aim for something less expensive, at least to start with.

The convenience of having an aeroplane available as and when you want to fly, without having to book ahead or wait for ages at the club for one to come free for half an hour, is a valuable plus point to some pilots. The fact that you can take your own machine away for the day, or the weekend (or for half a year, should that happen to be what you want) without anyone muttering about minimum flying hours requirements, appeals greatly to others. Knowing exactly how the aircraft has been treated at all times, being able to keep your own headsets, life jackets, charts and other gear in it, never finding someone else's sticky chocolate wrappers or smelly cigarette ends in the cockpit when you open it up, are all advantages that are appreciated by many owner pilots. Being fully familiar with all your own aeroplane's quirks, knowing instinctively how the radios and other avionics work, where the control lock is stowed and where the sick bags are hidden, being aware of how much oil and fuel it burns, all are factors that make flying your own aircraft much easier and more pleasurable than switching from one rented machine to another. It is impossible to measure any of these factors in strictly financial terms. That is perhaps just as well, since without consciously or subconsciously using these unquantifiable to counterbalance the hard facts produced by financial calculations, I have to admit that not many private pilots would ever become aircraft owners.

One of the nice things about owning your own machine is that when you come back to fly it you always find it just as clean and fresh as when you left it. It doesn't have overflowing ashtrays or cuts and stains on the upholstery and all your own equipment such as first aid kit, life jackets, headsets etc, are all exactly where you left them.

The cost of aircraft ownership can be calculated in many ways, some more honest than others. You can look at the results either as an annual cost of ownership or, to make a comparison with renting, as a cost per flying hour. Paradoxically, it is necessary for you to spend more in total on your flying if you want to reduce the actual hourly cost. The reason is that, once you take the plunge into ownership, you are saddled with costs that must be borne whether or not you fly the thing at all. These include items like hangar (or tie down) charges, insurance, depreciation and the annual inspection and C of A (or permit to fly) renewal. These so called 'fixed' costs do actually vary enormously depending on where your base aerodrome is located, what type of aircraft you purchase, whether you do some of the maintenance work yourself and whether your pride and joy lives under cover in a hangar or out in the open air. For the sake of argument, take these fixed costs as a hypothetical figure of £6,000 per annum for a four-seat 180hp single. Then, assuming you was to fly it for no more than 40 hours during an average year, the fixed costs alone would amount to £150 per flying hour, before you even start to look at the direct costs. These direct costs include not just the obvious the fuel and oil, but also building up a reserve for engine replacement, 50 hour checks, landing charges etc, and all these could very easily bring your hourly rate up to well over the £200 per hour mark. That makes hiring a club aircraft look like a terrific bargain. It also shows why, if you don't intend logging many hours each year, you should very carefully weigh up how highly you personally value all the above unquantifiable advantages of ownership, before you decide to buy.

On the other hand, once you own your own plane, you will almost certainly be automatically encouraged to do more flying than you would do in rented aircraft. After all, you will reason, you are then paying all these fixed costs anyway, so the only extra expenditure an hour in the air is going to cost you, are the direct costs. If (as often) your hangar/tie down rent includes local landings, these costs could be as little as £20 to £30 for an hour of local flying in a fuel economical light aircraft. If you then fly 150 hours a year, instead of the 40 suggested above, the fixed cost element shrinks from £150 to around £40 per flying hour, and now you are beginning to be significantly in pocket, compared with renting a similar aircraft. In addition, of course, you still have all the other advantages of ownership thrown in 'free of charge'. There is no way the writer can suggest where the breakpoint in annual flying hours is likely to lie in your own case. There are just too many variables involved. But these hypothetical figures at least show that it is well worth your while doing some serious sums. Don't just jot down some figures on the back of an envelope, and let them convince you that it is time you started seriously scrutinising the Aircraft for Sale advertisements in GA Buyer or at the back of Pilot Magazine. Be absolutely sure that you can afford to keep your winged mistress, before you commit yourself to any purchase. There aren't many things that take the joy out of flying quite so effectively, as a growing pile of final demand statements that you simply can't afford to pay.

The classified Aircraft for Sale pages in, for example, GA Buyer or Pilot Magazine are a good place to start the search for an aeroplane of your own

Aim a Little Lower

If the first set of calculations you make appears to show that you cannot justify that beautiful big aeroplane of your own on which you had set your heart, there probably still is a way round the problem. Many car drivers setting out to buy their first vehicle do rather fancy the idea of a high power, high performance luxury sports coupe with every possible bolt on goody already bolted on. They usually end up, never the less, with second-hand, ex-sales reps, 1,300cc bog standard saloon. Perhaps you should set your sights on something lower than that 'ideal flying machine' of yours; consider something less exotic and less expensive, so that it might blend in with your budget a little better. That could make a big difference to insurance costs as well as fuel and amortisation. It might also be worth considering keeping your aircraft at a different airfield, perhaps a little farther to drive to, but saving money on hangarage, tie downs, landing charges and maybe even fuel. However, being realistic about things, if your estimated utilisation of your own aeroplane is less than 100 hours, a year it is extremely unlikely that, whichever way you juggle the figures, you will ever be able to justify owning it, purely on an accountancy basis. You must then just decide for yourself how much extra you are willing to pay for every hour of flying in order to get all the other undoubted advantages that being the owner of your own aircraft brings.

How to Pick the Right Aeroplane

The Concise Oxford Dictionary defines an aeroplane as 'a mechanically driven heavier than air flying machine'. In the context of buying one for your own use a far better definition is that an aeroplane is 'a series of incompatible compromises'. You have to trade a comfortably wide cabin against lower cruising speed; a stable cruise against sluggish handling; size against cost; fuel efficiency against speed and so on. There isn't such a thing as a perfect aeroplane. The trick in aircraft buying is to pick the aeroplane whose design limitations are going to affect you least in the areas that matter most to you.

The world is full of people who seem to select their cars because one of their main aims is to "keep up with the Joneses". You can use this principle when you are looking for an aeroplane too, but believe me, it isn't the best way to pick a plane that is going to suit you. If you don't get a real buzz from the look of little aeroplanes, if you don't find yourself feeling at least a little bit emotional about them, then you had better forget the whole idea of being an owner. Just keep on renting for those occasional flights when you want to be the pilot and the rest of the time use your car, or an airliner for your longer trips. If aeroplanes do turn you on and you really have the urge to own one, you must still try not to let your emotions play too big a part in the selection process. You have to feel good about the plane when you see it; to feel that you are really going to enjoy sharing the skies with it. Not just for today or next month, but for next year and very probably for a good few years longer than that too.

An elegantly designed, inexpensive to operate machine like this two seat Diamond Aircraft HK36D Super Dimona
with its Rotax engine could be an attractive choice for many would-be private owners, especially pilots who like to
combine powered flight with gliding.

Is it the right machine for the sort of flying you want to do? Does it have enough space for
the family, enough range to get to where you are likely frequently to be going? Even if you lust
after a high horsepower mean machine you must try to be practical and remember how often
you really need to get in and out of short grass strips to do the things you really enjoy doing. If
your dream is of operating from grass fields under blue cloudless skies and pottering quietly
along enjoying the view below you, don't forget that if you make more than the occasional long
flight (on business perhaps) then the ideal machine for the first sort of flying enjoyment will
probably be completely incompatible with these other requirements. When you are sizing up
your prospective purchase try to ask yourself all these practical questions, but don't forget that
the most important question of all probably is does it look like you are really going to enjoy it?

Decision Time

One of the first choices to be made is whether you want a single or a twin. The pros and cons
of twins were discussed in Chapter 6. If money is no object, if you expect to have to fly in icing
conditions and do a lot of your aviating over the sea or mountains then a twin just might possibly
make sense. But don't purchase one just for the prestige. Remember that, statistically, you have
twice the chance of experiencing engine failure in a twin and that anyone less than an
experienced and proficient multi engine pilot has less chance of surviving the failure of single
engine in a twin than most pilots have of surviving after losing their only engine in a single.

I am therefore assuming that for the majority of readers the decision here will be quite
decisively in favour of a single engine aeroplane. Then the next matter is to decide which single
is the right one for your particular needs and wants? The answer to this is often contained in
the prospective purchaser's bank book rather than the Pilot's Operating Handbook for the
aeroplane. What you would want in an ideal world and what is possible for you in practice are
often two entirely different things. But having determined where your financial limit lies, you
may well find that it is still difficult to know what that cash will buy. In America various

publications give guide prices for aircraft but in most European countries, the UK included, the market is too small for that to take place. The classified ads in the appropriate flying magazines do help to give a general guide, although advertisers there often seem to have somewhat optimistic ideas of what their aeroplanes are really worth. A bit of old fashioned negotiation (or haggling) frequently pays the purchaser handsomely.

Similar sounding aeroplanes change hands at very widely varying prices too, depending on such things as whether they have any damage history, what engine life is remaining, the state of the interior furnishings and that external paintwork, the value of the avionics fit and the age of the airframe. The American publications mentioned above can be useful reading for anyone contemplating following the often trodden path to the States to buy their aircraft there. The Aircraft Bluebook Digest, The A/C Flyer, Vref and The Aircraft Bulletin are useful sources of American used aircraft price information. There are also many pages of similar information available to download from the Internet.

If you live where it is possible to base your aircraft at one of the quieter airfields (such as North Connell ...

… or Haverfordwest here) the costs of hangarage and landing charges may well be significantly less than if you choose a busier, fully equipped airport as the home base for your own aircraft.

Thus, even when you know exactly how much money you have available (or can persuade someone to lend you) there is still a great deal of choosing and deciding to do. It is easier on the whole to buy from someone in the country where you live, but there are times when currency fluctuations seem to make importing an aircraft a very attractive financial proposition. The base price you pay for the aircraft then is, however, only the beginning. You must bear in mind that shipping or flying your new toy to the UK, and then having it prepared for acceptance onto the CAA's UK register, can be expensive exercises to carry out. Then who do you buy from? An agent, a broker or a private individual? Each has its advantages; each has its drawbacks. Again we come back to weighing these up from your own individual point of view and choosing what is best under your own particular circumstances.

Next comes the actual choice of aeroplane. What about size for a start? Not many pilots really need a six seat aircraft. Even if you do occasionally carry five passengers, the difference in running costs between a four and a six seat machine will probably be enough to pay for the rent of a six seater on the odd occasions you actually require one. In the other direction you may be mulling over the idea of a single seat aircraft for overall economy. Undoubtedly most of these are very much cheaper to buy and fly than two or four seat aircraft, but is that really the only consideration for you? One seat is very limiting. You can fly solo in a two seat aircraft but you can't take a passenger in a single seater, and flying does sometimes tend to get just a trife lonesome when every flight is another enforced solo.

High wing or low wing is generally a matter of personal choice. If Piper trained, you will probably have a predilection for low wing aircraft; Cessna trained pilots have a tendency to go in the other direction. There are technical arguments about high wing aircraft being more stable because their C of G is below the centre of lift and therefore they give a better ride in turbulence. They also give everyone a better view of the ground; at least until you as pilot really need a good view while you bank as you turn onto base leg and final while approaching to land, when the wing tends to obscure just what you want to see. Personal preferences and prejudices play a bigger part here than any aerodynamic theories; until they start building Boeing and Airbus airliners as well as supersonic military aircraft with their wings above their pilots' heads I personally shall continue to be happier myself while piloting low wing aeroplanes.

Another question to which there is no clear cut technical answer is whether you should buy a metal aeroplane, a wooden one, or one of these sexy, curvaceous aircraft made by bonding together foam cores, pre-preg glass fibre and carbon fibre composite materials. Each has its advantages and disadvantages. If that were not so you would not be likely to find aeronautical engineers still arguing over their relative merits and still designing new aircraft for production in each of these three types of material. There is no doubt though, that the majority of the second hand machines you will have to choose from will turn out to be of metal construction, so the probability is that, unless you make a determined effort to go for one of the other materials, it is a metal aeroplane that you are going to end up owning.

If you intend doing a great deal of your flying at high altitude, a turbocharged aircraft might be worth considering. Otherwise you would be better to leave these designs strictly alone. For the majority of owners the extra fuel which turbocharged aircraft burn and the extra maintenance costs they bring, can negate any speed and climb advantages they might have. Likewise, unless you are one of these people who feel you just have to be different, steer clear of anything too exotic. Some unusual aircraft are difficult to insure for a start. Some may be fine until you need a spare and find that parts just don't exist any more. If you are not yourself a competent DIY person, but despite that fact you still decide take a chance and buy someone else's home built aircraft, you may well find it very tricky to find any mechanics that will be prepared to maintain it for you.

Make a sensible analysis of what you want your aeroplane to do for you. Consider the type of flying you are most likely to be doing, the loads you will want to carry and the minimum range you really require. Be realistic. There is little point in paying over the odds just to save a couple of refuelling stops on the occasional one or two really long flights you expect to make in the course of your average year's flying. It is too easy to fall into the trap of buying, on impulse, something with lots of bells and whistles that you are seldom, or never, going to make use of. Match your aircraft to your sensible requirements and you can save yourself a lot of money.

It is obviously always a good idea to fly the actual aircraft before you commit yourself to buying it. Less obvious perhaps is the thought that, even before you reach the stage of test flying your prospective purchase, it is an even more sensible idea to rent a similar model for one or two trips if you can. That way you and your partner and/or family can get a much better feel for how it is likely to match up to your requirements, and theirs. If you have a strong inclination towards one particular type of aircraft it is often worth finding out whether there is an active owners' club. These organisations often publish useful newsletters or magazines giving hints and tips about problems other owners have encountered and how these can best be overcome. The information coming from owners clubs is often a lot more accurate and informative, especially concerning performance figures, than even the data published by the manufacturers. These maker's brochure figures are really a form of advertising, and usually refer to brand new aircraft flown by super competent pilots under ideal conditions. So far as performance is concerned, there is little point either in trying to obtain your data from 'independent' sources like Pilot or Flyer magazine flight reports or Jane's All the World's Aircraft because, with very few exceptions, the figures in these publications too are usually derived from the manufacturers' own suspiciously optimistic publicity.

The Microlight Alternative

There is now another class of aircraft on the scene which tends to make the prospective purchaser's decision that much harder. These are the microlights or, as they are referred to in many other countries, ultralights. Differing from the conventional light aircraft on which you learned to fly mainly in terms of size, weight and fuel capacity, they represent an opportunity of getting into ownership of a single or two seat aircraft, for a significantly lower investment than a conventional two seat aircraft. Microlights started off as little more than hang-gliders with power units, but they have developed a long way since then and some of the three axis control microlights (these are the ones that look more or less like normal light aircraft) can be flown by anyone who holds a JAA PPL (A).

It is advisable though, to have a microlight pilot at least check you out first, and it would probably be even better for you if you did a proper microlight conversion course. Some of these machines have special characteristics of their own which come as a bit of a surprise to pilots who have been accustomed to nothing other than a basic Piper or Cessna trainer. On the other hand, some microlights are almost indistinguishable in their handling from normal aircraft. Indeed some designs are available in two different versions; one classified as a microlight and another as a light aeroplane. Many are also available in kit form for home building. The capital cost of a microlight can be much less than that of a normal aircraft, but the new price of some top of the range microlights is appreciably more than you would need to pay for a reasonably good, even if well used, second hand conventional two seat aircraft. It is in the running costs that microlights really score. They sip much less fuel, are less costly to maintain, can be hangared cheaply (often in a trailer or garage) and landing fees for them are generally very low. If your aircraft ownership ambitions are bigger than your bank balance, it could certainly be worth making contact with the British Microlight Aircraft Association. They will put you right on all you need to know about this interesting and economical branch of private flying.

Some flex wing microlight aircraft may look flimsy, but are in fact very capable little aeroplanes, offering many pilots an inexpensive entry into the ranks of aircraft ownership.

Other designs of microlight and recreational aircraft, like this Aeroprakt A22 Foxbat, are quite difficult to distinguish from conventional single engine light aircraft, either when looking at them from the outside or when you are in the cockpit piloting them.

Check Before Cheque

Unless you are technically qualified you should get an engineer you know and can trust to give your potential purchase a thorough inspection. This must include compression checking each cylinder, a corrosion (or glue joint) inspection, a cross check of aircraft and component serial numbers (to make sure you aren't buying stolen property) and a good read through the logbooks etc, to ensure no documents are missing and that there aren't any expensive Airworthiness Directives (ADs) or service bulletins that haven't been complied with. Ideally, your friendly engineer should be pretty conversant with the type of aircraft you are buying. Almost any fault in an aeroplane can be put right, but skilled engineers' time doesn't come cheap so if the machine you are considering has something wrong with it make doubly sure that any estimated repair costs are realistic. Once the aircraft becomes your property, it is you who will have to pay these bills. Don't be misled though, by too dismal prognostications from your engineer about previous repairs; like dentists and hairdressers, many aviation engineers just love to criticise the work that other people have done.

Once you have finally decided on the aircraft of your dreams, do your utmost to make sure the owner has a clear title to it, free from any outstanding loans, co-owners, or other financial encumbrances. Then, after you have negotiated a mutually satisfactory price, arranged any necessary finance and agreed the date you take over the keys of your very own aeroplane, don't be in so much of a hurry to fly it away that you forget to arrange insurance cover. Even a minor mishap in the course of an uninsured delivery flight could completely spoil the start of your life as an aircraft owner.

Building your Own Aeroplane

The 'do it yourself' route into aircraft ownership is an attractive one from many points of view. There are many good looking and capable designs of aeroplane now available for home construction. The range of aircraft that can be self built under LAA supervision, and flown on Permit, has been extended during the 1990s to include four seaters and aircraft fitted with higher horsepower engines than formerly was allowed. This is a far cry from a few decades back when a home built was nearly always a slow, low power contraption with an ugly boxy looking fuselage and a rectangular wing that looked as though it had been temporarily glued on either above or below it.

Home building has a long and, on the whole, honourable history. The idea really got off the ground in France in the inter-war years when Henri Mignet designed the Pou du Ciel, known as the 'Flying Flea' in English speaking countries (where the literal translation 'Louse of the Skies' somehow didn't have quite the right ring about it). A series of articles in Practical Mechanics described how the Flea could be flown by just about anyone, and gave details of how it could be built in a garage using no more than a simple set of tools. The enthusiasm for this idea was the catalyst that brought the Ultra Light Aircraft Association (ULAA) into being in Britain. It had the blessing of the authorities to help enthusiasts to design and build their own aircraft. The Pou du Ciel, alas, was not quite the great success its designer had anticipated. However, members of the ULAA did produce quite a few respectable little aircraft of other designs before World War II came along and put an abrupt end to their activities. In 1946 the ULAA came back to life again, albeit under its new name, the Popular Flying Association (PFA), which since 2008 has been known as the Light Aircraft Association (LAA). It is to the LAA that anyone in the United Kingdom wanting to build an aircraft of his or her own must turn. Those interested might also find it worth joining the American Experimental Aircraft Association (EAA) as well, to keep in touch with the tremendous strides in home building that have been made in recent years in the USA and to get their excellent newsletters. The LAA's own magazine Light Aviation is also a first class monthly publication for anyone intending to tackle the task of putting together an aircraft of his or her own.

Typical of the good looking designs now available for home construction is this sleek Vans RV-6 which has a performance to match its sexy lines.

The LAA can let members have details of all the kits that are approved for construction in the UK and it has been designated by the CAA to oversee the design and construction, or restoration, of aircraft by private individuals. It is only by satisfying the quality requirements of the LAA's team of inspectors that anything you build yourself will be granted a Permit to Fly, without which it has to stay firmly on terra firma. So if you want to build your own aeroplane, then the earlier you contact the LAA the better are your chances of ultimate success. The LAA's Permit to Fly is the home built aircraft's counterpart of the CAA's Certificate of Airworthiness (C of A) or a commercially manufactured aircraft. It has, however, several limitations in comparison with a C of A, and these are worth considering carefully before you embark on this route to ownership. Some Permit aircraft are not allowed to fly over built up areas, except as necessary for landing and taking off. The Permit is not valid outside the UK, so any flights abroad will require prior clearance from the appropriate foreign authorities. (Normally this is just an inconvenient formality, as permission is usually freely granted.) You will not be permitted to fly at night, nor over built up areas, nor in IMC, and you are not allowed to use a Permit aircraft for any training, except the training of a pilot who is the owner or part owner of the aeroplane.

Modern Designs and Materials

Home building has become less daunting for amateur aircraft engineers in recent years, with the introduction of modern construction materials and techniques such as Kevlar, carbon fibre, composite foam and glass fibre. These innovations have, to some extent at least, reduced the need for technical skills in tin bashing or woodworking. Home built aircraft have also gained considerably in reliability in recent years with the advent of better power units than the old converted Volkswagen flat fours and McCullochs. The Rotax range of two and four stroke engines in particular is proving very popular and reliable, whilst other home built aircraft fly with a wide range of engines; Continental, Lycoming, Limbach, Subaru and new designs like the Zoche diesel range, the Australian Jabiru, the rotary Wankels etc. Home building is not the preserve only of anorak clad tinkerers and cranks, nor is it restricted solely to expert craftsmen and women. That said, unless you are one of those people who really enjoy building things, the chances of you making a successful entry into the world of home building are rather slender. On the other hand, lack of experience is no bar; few people who start their own DIY aeroplane have ever built one before though some gluttons for punishment are known to have actually built with their own hands four or more of these machines. You will almost certainly have to be prepared to learn some new skills but specialist aspects of the work such as welding, if required, are probably best left to experts. You might also experience a different sort of problem if you opt for one of the 'easier' designs that involve working with epoxy resins, glass fibre and bonding agents. You could find that you are one of those unfortunate people who are allergic to the chemicals and solvents in some of these things.

This is a Jabiru light aircraft engine, one of the many modern and reliable designs of petrol and diesel power units that are now available for home builders to fit to their self constructed aircraft.

Why do People do It?

Why would anyone ever want to build an aircraft of their own? Some people take this route so that they can have a design of aircraft that satisfies their requirements better than any production aeroplane they can find. Some because they feel they will get more machine for less of their money this way. Others simply because they want to enjoy the immense satisfaction of constructing something really worthwhile with their own hands, and then following that with the exhilarating feeling of actually taking to the air in something that they themselves have just built.

Those in the third of these categories are the ones most likely to achieve their aim. Those in the first category might be lucky too. But the ones who get into home building mainly in order to save money are liable to be disappointed. A set of plans and the material needed to build an aeroplane to the required design, certainly come a whole lot cheaper than a completed aeroplane. That much goes without saying. But to get the materials transmogrified into a flying machine takes endless hours of labour. Your own labour you may choose to disregard so far as cost is concerned but outside labour and workshop space, light and heating, all have to be budgeted for. Make one tiny and apparently insignificant mistake with an expensive sheet of plywood or plastic or aluminium and that can put up the building costs too. Very few people construct aeroplanes direct from plans these days. They buy kits, and these invariably work out rather more expensive than basic raw materials. Kits do, of course, have the valuable attribute of being quite a lot quicker to turn into finished aeroplanes. All in all, the true finished cost of a self-built light aeroplane is likely to be appreciably more than the cost of a similar second hand machine in fair to good condition. But no second hand aircraft is ever going to give you the same rewards as that ultimate thrill of getting into the air at the controls of something you lovingly created with your own hands.

It All Takes Time

Concerning build time, don't embark on this sort of project without thinking this factor through carefully. Most kit manufacturers quote a suggested build time for their kits. Most members of LAA will tell you that, as a first-time builder, you are going to find these times totally unattainable. If the kit claims that 'only' 1,000 man hours are needed to construct it, take that with a pinch of salt. Call it at least 1,250 or perhaps closer to 1,500 hours. Ask other LAA members who have built the design in question and you'll get a better feel for the time that actually is likely to be involved. If it turns out to be 1,500 hours that may not sound much when you say it quickly, but it translates into a whole lot of your life. It means, for instance, that if you work on your kit for two hours a day, every day, weekends included, it will take you 750 days. So if you do your two hours per day religiously, then put in an extra few hours most weekends and don't take any holidays for the next two full calendar years, you should just about manage to complete it in that time. It takes dedication. It takes something else for married people too; an understanding, sympathetic and perhaps even helpful spouse. Are you sure she (or he) will accept wood shavings and glue smells in the kitchen, epoxy resin curing in the lounge, your absence, hour upon hour every evening, the noise of drilling or riveting drowning the Mozart on the hi-fl or the sound from the television?

Changed Lifestyle

It is pretty obvious then, that building your own aeroplane the DIY way is going to make hefty inroads into the rest of your life. Something has to give; any other hobbies, certainly; much of your flying, probably. Evenings in front of the television or at the cinema will become rarities; the garden could turn into a wilderness, so far as you are concerned; what the rest of the world knows as DIY (that plebeian stuff with shelves, paint and wallpaper around the house) will have to take a back seat. Are you and your partner (if any) really prepared to make that sort of sacrifice? If you're honest answer is 'yes', then go ahead and good luck to you. You could be embarking on a project that will probably bring you more real satisfaction than any other hobby you could take up. People who have succeeded in getting their home built aircraft completed and into the air will tell you (and anyone else in their vicinity who is prepared to listen) just what a feeling of achievement that has brought them, and how amply it compensates for all the years of hard work and hardship that went before the flying. If however you frankly don't feel you are ready to make the sacrifices involved and aren't sure you'll be able to devote so much of your time to the project, then go back to the previous section of this chapter and start looking for a ready made machine. Just because you aren't prepared to dedicate the next two years or so of your life to sanding and sawing, bending metal or bonding mastic, there is no need to give up on all the thrills and joys of doing your flying in your very own aeroplane.

The Next Best Thing – Group Flying

You have perhaps added up the costs of building your own aeroplane and decided that the time, the work or the money involved is more than you can afford. You have studied the prices of the production aircraft in GA Buyer and in the Pilot and Flyer classified aircraft for sale adverts but sadly, once you compared these with your available cash, you have concluded that purely for financial reasons you and aircraft ownership don't seem to quite match. But don't give up on the whole idea at that stage. There still is another way of getting onto aircraft ownership. Don't decide just yet that you will just have to continue to book ahead to hire the tired old club Cessna, as and when you and it happens to be free at the same time.

Instead, you could join a Group. Or you could even form one.

Group flying combines many of the advantages of private ownership with some of those of club flying. And admittedly it also combines certain of the disadvantages of both. The traditional flying Group is made up of a few pilots who have come together to share the flying of an aeroplane which none of them individually could afford to buy or operate. The pilots making up the Group probably all fly mainly for fun, rather than for business, and each is prepared to pay his or her own share of the fixed costs involved. Each must also be willing to do something towards the chores involved in aircraft ownership, and to get together as partners and friends every so often to elect office bearers, transact Group business, and generally enjoy each others' company.

Sharing an Interest

The principle of getting together with several other people to do Group flying may perhaps seem just a little anachronistic. After all in today's world people are more accustomed to the beggar your neighbour attitudes of the rat race, to families who rarely even sit down to eat together and to general apathy towards many community activities. Despite that, in terms of making it possible to enjoy what is tantamount to private use of an aeroplane, for much less capital outlay and considerably lower running costs, there is a great deal to be said in favour of Groups. The big proviso is that the pilots involved must get along well together and should all contribute something more than just cash to the running of the group. Group flying can then quite adequately fill the awkward gap that yawns between the frustrations of renting from a club, and committing yourself to the expense of full ownership.

A single private owner often ends up by flying relatively little and so the utilisation of the aircraft is poor, leading to exorbitant hourly costs when all the amortisation, insurance and other fixed costs are considered. A few pilots could band together around that same aircraft, shove the utilisation up to say 400 hours per annum, and so bring down drastically the share of the fixed costs that each flying hour must bear. It also enables a Group of like minded pilots to fly something more interesting than the aeroplanes likely to be on offer from local flying clubs. Instead of a basic two seat trainer or a typical club operated four seat tourer, the group could fly an old timer or an aerobatic machine if the pilots had a mind to, or a higher speed tourer like a Bonanza or Mooney perhaps. Alternatively it could head for a lower performance, less expensive model to keep down fuel and overall operating costs.

A Group aircraft provides its members with regular access to a familiar cockpit. Club pilots have to fly whichever aircraft happens to be free in whatever condition the last user left it. As a member of a Group, you will fly what is your own aeroplane (at least in part) and all the others who also fly it are again part owners. They will, you trust, also have a proprietarily interest equal to your own in keeping the machine in good condition. On the other hand Group membership involves you in more than just walking up to the operations desk at the club and asking for the keys. You are expected to take on some of the chores of ownership, like helping to wash and wax the bird, keeping the engine and airframe logs up to date, organising the Group activities (social and otherwise), keeping the books, collecting dues, writing and distributing Group communications, paying the bills, ensuring that routine servicing and maintenance are done, etc.

Many successful Groups are formed around a standard, simply maintained and easy to fly aeroplane like a Cessna 172, Piper PA-28 or Grumman AA5

Good Rules – Secrets of Success

If you join an established Group or answer one of the advertisements in Pilot, Light Aviation, and Flyer etc where someone is trying to form a Group, you will have to accept, by and large, the existing rules and regulations. When it is you who is forming a new Group with some fellow pilots, you have to devise a suitable format for your Group. It can be a cost sharing Group around one privately owned aircraft, where members contribute towards the overheads and pay a basic hourly rate for flying. Alternatively, each member may become a part owner of the aircraft and each flies it paying the basic direct costs. There are various rather complicated CAA rules and insurance requirements that affect this decision and these should be carefully considered before the Group constitution is drawn up. The LAA website www.lightaircraftassociation.co.uk can be a useful source of ideas about how to write your Group constitution.

The number of members in the Group is another important point to consider. Too few and the main objective of improving utilisation to reduce flying costs may not be achieved. Too many and you will be back to the old flying club problem of getting hold of the aircraft when you want it. This becomes especially tricky if the members are all the type of pilots who prefer to fly in the summer and then usually on Sunday afternoons. About five or six pilots is probably a good number to aim for. That is usually enough to cope with the various chores involved without anyone being overloaded with work, and not so many as to make scheduling the aircraft too difficult at busy times. If the majority of members are interested in flying long trips, four or five should be the maximum allowed to join. If most members fly in the main, local pleasure trips only, then there should be room for a few more, especially if some members are able to do most of their flying mid week. Membership dues should be invoiced each month to cover all the costs that tick relentlessly on whether a member flies or not. Some Groups make it compulsory for each member to pay for one hour's flying with his or her monthly dues. That payment is forfeited to the Group if the member doesn't fly his or her hour during the month in question. The idea behind this is to give an incentive to all members to keep themselves in flying practice and maintain their proficiency, but if it fails in that aim, it at least compensates the Group financially for the reduced utilisation of the aircraft.

When the question of finance was under discussion in Chapter 5, it was mentioned that there was one special set of circumstances, associated with Group flying, in which a private pilot can legally accept payment in connection with his or her flying. This is in the case of a flight in a jointly owned aircraft; the payment involved must reflect the actual costs of the flight and must be made by one of the joint owners to another. Joint ownership in this case cannot involve more than twenty people and each joint owner must own at least a 5% share in the aircraft.

Choosing your fellow members in the Group is important. It isn't everyone who makes a good 'Groupie' and letting a "wrong 'un" join the Group can have a distinctly adverse effect on everyone else involved. Your Group almost certainly will lack a psychologist to vet all applicants, but you should at least get each would be member to fill in a fairly thorough questionnaire with details of not just their name, address and telephone numbers but also such items as their flying experience, occupation, credit and personal references and what they expect to do with the Group aircraft. It is well worth the trouble to try to run a credit check on the applicants. Some may object to this, but it is far better to lose a potential member at that stage than to end up with a problem member. It has been known for plausible types to turn up, join a Group that doesn't do adequate checking, run up a bill for several hundred pounds worth of flying and then vanish without trace. The cost of their flying unfortunately doesn't vanish with them; it has to be borne by the remaining members. Some Groups run into trouble if the rules allow any member leaving to sell his or her share directly to anybody else he or she chooses. It is safer to incorporate some clause making it compulsory to offer the share back to the Group first, or at least to allow the other members to blackball any potential replacement member they regard as unsuitable. To make things run smoothly, each Group needs officials to look after various jobs. A treasurer, a secretary and a safety officer are almost essential. General management, and looking after technical matters like maintenance of the aircraft, may be included in the duties of one or other of these, or may be allocated to another member or members.

Sometimes Group members have a special interest in flying a tail wheel aeroplane such as this Auster or perhaps one that is capable of performing aerobatics like a Pitts Special, a Yak or a Zlin

Plane for all Members

Having got the Group formed, or at least having established that there are sufficient suitable people who are interested in the formation of a Group, the all important next step is to select an aircraft to suit the needs of the membership and which is within the financial reach of the Group. Is it to be used mainly locally or for longer trips? IFR or VFR? Does it need to be suitable for landing on and taking off from short runways? Should it be stressed for aerobatics? How many seats? Is cruising speed more important to members than fuel consumption, or is it the other way round? Think long and hard over factors such as these, otherwise the Group could get landed with what might well be a beautiful aeroplane, but one that is incompatible with the needs of most of the members. If that happens it simply won't get used enough and ultimately an unsuitable machine is very liable to cause the Group to fail. Another common cause of Group troubles is the financial problem that can arise from under capitalisation. Then there is always the danger of unanticipated unserviceability of the Group aircraft. This can interrupt flying and the associated cash flow that flying generates which is normally essential for the viability of the Group. The aircraft unserviceability can also perhaps cost rather more to rectify than the group can afford to pay. For this reason it is sensible to try to build up some form of reserve or contingency fund in the Group's bank balance and to insist that all members settle their accounts for flying promptly.

It does take quite a bit of work to organise and run a Group operation successfully, but the rewards can be sweet. As a member of a non profit-making organisation you should be able to fly for appreciably less cost than if you were still hiring from a commercially run school or club. You will certainly be able to fly for significantly less cost per hour than if you were the sole owner of the same aeroplane. You are likely to build up close friendships with a number of people whose interests are similar to your own, and each one of you can enjoy having realised your cherished dream of 'owning an aeroplane' without needing to bear all of the overhead expenses on your own. If you are ready to surrender just a little of your independence by going into partnership with some fellow pilots, you stand to gain a great deal more than you lose.

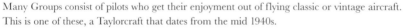

Many Groups consist of pilots who get their enjoyment out of flying classic or vintage aircraft. This is one of these, a Taylorcraft that dates from the mid 1940s.

Conclusion

Only a few of the private pilots who read this book are likely ever to have opportunities to participate in more than three or four of the different types of flying that have been described in these chapters. Nevertheless, most PPL holders could derive a great deal of extra pleasure and satisfaction from their licences simply by making an effort to take part in each of these suggestions that happens to appeal to them.

It is only by branching out from time to time into new and challenging fields of flying that private pilots can ever get full value from the substantial investment they made in qualifying for their PPLs in the first place. All of us who have been fortunate enough to turn piloting into an important part of our lives probably started out with little more than a vague dream of flight. Unlike the many men and women who once had that dream somewhere in the back of their heads but never believed that they could actually learn to fly, we belong to the privileged minority who took on the challenge and who managed to turn that early dream of flight into a reality. When we first made it come alive we were just taking tentative steps along what soon developed into a fascinating and rewarding journey.

If *Clearer Horizons* helps to encourage even a minority of its readers to investigate a few of these avenues of aviation which they might otherwise never have explored, the book will have served its purpose. Its author has obtained an immense amount of pleasure and satisfaction from piloting military and civil aircraft during the sixty years that have now passed since he made his first flight. His aim in sharing these ideas, suggestions and experiences is to help readers to get as much enjoyment out of piloting in all its varied aspects as he has been lucky enough to do.

Flying often involves a complex mixture of emotions and events. Every pilot loves it at some times and loathes it at others. It is full of pitfalls and disappointments but these I have always found are more than compensated for by the delights, successes, excitement and exhilaration. There are occasional times in almost every pilot's life when he or she feels a bit like throwing in the towel. If one of these times ever does come along in your own flying life, why not just leave that towel where it is? Take this book off the bookshelf again and somewhere in its pages you'll surely find another flying challenge to tackle, something more that will help keep your beautiful dream alive.

Abbreviations

aal	Above Aerodrome Level
ADF	Automatic Direction Finding
agl	Above Ground Level
AI	Attitude Indicator (or Artificial Horizon)
AIC	Aeronautical Information Circular
AIP	Aeronautical Information Publication (UK version also known as 'Air Pilot')
AIS	Aeronautical Information Service
amsl	Above Mean Sea Level
ANO	Air Navigation Order (UK)
AOA	Aerodrome Owners' Association
AOC	Air Operator's Certificate
AOPA	Aircraft Owners and Pilots' Association
ASI	Airspeed Indicator
ATC	Air Traffic Control
ATIS	Automatic Terminal Information Service
ATPL	Airline Transport Pilot's Licence
ATZ	Aerodrome Traffic Zone
BAeA	British Aerobatic Association
BWPA	British Women Pilots' Association
CAA	Civil Aviation Authority
CAD	Computer Aided Design
CAP	Civil Air Publication
CAS	Calibrated Airspeed
CDI	Course Deviation Indicator
C of A	Certificate of Airworthiness
C of G	Centre of Gravity
CPL	Commercial Pilot's Licence
CTR	Control Zone
DAAIS	Danger Area Activity Information Service
DACS	Danger Area Crossing Service
DI	Directional Indicator or Gyro Compass
DME	Distance Measuring Equipment
EAA	Experimental Aircraft Association (USA)
EASA	European Aviation Safety Agency
EGT	Exhaust Gas Temperature (Gauge)
ETA	Estimated Time of Arrival
FAA	Federal Aviation Authority (USA)
FAI	Fédération Aéronautique Internationale
FBO	Fixed Base Operator
FCL	Flight Crew Licensing
FI	Flight Instructor

FI(R)	Flight Instructor (restricted)
FIR	Flight Information Region
FIS	Flight Information Service
FL	Flight Level
FPL	Flight Plan
GA	General Aviation
GFT	General Flight Test
GLONASS	Global Navigation Satellite System (Russian)
GPS	Global Positioning System (USA)
HASELL CHECK	Vital actions before aerobatics etc
	Height, Airframe, Security, Engine, Location and Look out
HSI	Horizontal Situation Indicator
IAS	Indicated Air Speed
IAOPA	International Council of Aircraft Owners and Pilots Associations
ICAO	International Civil Aviation Organisation
IF	Instrument Flight
IFR	Instrument Flight Rules
IMC	Instrument Meteorological Conditions
IR	Instrument Rating
JAA	Joint Airworthiness Authority (Europe)
JAR	Joint Airworthiness Requirements (Europe)
LAA	Light Aircraft Association
LAAS	Local Area Augmentation System
LARS	Lower Airspace Radar Service
LCD	Liquid Crystal Display
MATZ	Military Aerodrome Traffic Zone
METAR	Meteorological Aerodrome Report
MHz	Megahertz (106 cycles/second)
MSA	Minimum Safe (or Sector) Altitude
NDB	Non-Directional Beacon
OAT	Outside Air Temperature
OBI	Omni-bearing Indicator
PC	Personal Computer
POH	Pilot's Operating Handbook
PPL	Private Pilot's Licence
PPR	Prior Permission Required
QFE	Altimeter setting to give height above aerodrome
QNH	Altimeter setting that gives the aircraft's altitude above mean sea level
RAeC	Royal Aero Club
RAIM	Receiver Autonomous Integrity Monitoring
RAS	Rectified Air Speed
RBI	Relative Bearing Indicator
RT	Radiotelephony

SID	Standard Instrument Departure
SR	Sunrise
SS	Sunset
STAR	Standard Instrument Arrival
SVFR	Special Visual Flight Rules
TAF	Terminal Aerodrome Forecast
TAS	True Air Speed
TMA	Terminal Manoeuvring Area
ULAA	Ultra-light Aircraft association
VAT	Value Added Tax
VFR	Visual Flight Rules
VHF	Very High Frequency
VMC	Visual Meteorological Conditions
VOLMET	VHF Met Report broadcast for aircraft in flight
VOR	VHF Omni-directional Range Radio Beacon
VRP	Visual Reporting Point
WAAS	Wide Area Augmentation System

Useful Aviation Addresses

Aeronautical Information Service
NATS, AIS Central Office
First Floor
Control Tower Building
London Heathrow Airport
Hounslow
Middlesex
TW6 1JJ
Tel: 020 8745 3456
www.ais.org.uk

Airplan Flight Equipment (AFE)
1a Ringway Trading Estate
Shadowmoss Road
Manchester
M22 5LH
Tel: 0161 499 0023
Fax: 0161 499 0298
www.afeonline.com

AOPA (UK)
50a Cambridge Street
London
SWIV 4QQ
Tel: 020 7834 5631
Fax: 020 7834 8623
www.aopa.co.uk

AOPA (USA) also for International
Partnership
421 Aviation Way
Frederick
Maryland MD 21701-9922
USA
Tel: +001 301 695 2000
Fax: +001 301 695 2375

Aviatours (Charter) Ltd
Pinewoods, Eglinton Road
Rushmore, Farnham
Surrey
GU10 2DH
Tel: 01252 793250

British Aerobatic Association (BAA)
White Waltham Airfield
Maidenhead
Berkshire
SL6 3NJ
Tel: 01455 617211
www.aerobatics.org.uk

British Hanggliding and Paragliding Association (BHPA)
The Old School Room
Loughborough Road
Leicester
LE4 5PG
Tel: 0116 2611322
www.bhpa.co.uk

British Microlight Aircraft Association (BMAA)
Bullring
Deddington
Oxfordshire
OX5 4TT
Tel: 01869 338888
www.bmaa.org

British Precision Pilots' Association (BPPA)
Kenvale
Northview Avenue
Bideford
Devon
EX39 3LH
Tel: 01237 471529
www.rallyflyingclub.org

British Women Pilots' Association (BWPA)
Brooklands Museum
Weybridge
Surrey
KT13 OQN
Tel: 01342 892739
www.bwpa.org.uk

British Business and General Aviation Association
19 Church Street
Brill
Aylesbury
HP18 9RT
Tel: 01844 238020
Fax: 01844 238087
info@bbga.aero
www.bbga.aero

Civil Aviation Authority (CAA)
CAA House
45-59 Kingsway
London
WC2B 6TE
Tel: 020 7379 7311
www.caa.co.uk

Civil Aviation Authority (CAA/FCL)
Flight Crew Licensing
Ground Floor
Aviation House
Gatwick Airport South
West Sussex
RH6 OYR
Tel: 01293 567171
www.caa.co.uk

Fédération Aéronautique Internationale (FAI)
Avenue Mon Repos 24
CH-1005 – Lausanne
Switzerland
Tel: +41 21 345 1070
Fax: +41 21 345 1077

Flying Farmers' Association (FFA)
Moor Farm
West Heslerton
Molton
North Yorkshire
YO17 8RU
Tel: 01944 738281
www.ffa.org.uk

General Aviation Safety Committee (GASCo)
Rochester Airport
Chatham
Kent
ME5 9SD
Tel: 01634 200203
www.gasco.org.uk

Light Aircraft Association (LAA)
Turweston Aerodrome
Brackley
Northants
NN13 5YD
Tel: 01280 846 786
Fax: 01280 846 780
www.lightaircraftassociation.co.uk

Pooleys
Elstree Aerodrome
Elstree
Hertfordshire
WD6 3AW
Tel: 020 8207 3749
Fax: 020 8953 2512
www.pooleys.com

Royal Aero Club (RAeC)
Radford Barn
Radford Semele
Leamington Spa
Warwickshire
CV31 1UT
Tel: 01926 332713
Fax: 01926 335206
www.royalaeroclub.org

Royal Aeronautical Society (RAES)
4 Hamilton Place
London W1
Tel: 020 7499 3456
www.raes.org.uk

Service de l'Information Aéronautique
91205 Athis-Mons
CEDEX
France
Tel: +69 84 56 03/04
Fax: +69 84 5602

Transair
Shoreham Airport
Shoreham by Sea
West Sussex
BN43 5PA
Tel: 01273 466000
www.transair.co.uk

Index